CW00551365

SAWS AND SAWING

SAWS AND SAWING

Ian Bradley

Special Interest Model Books

Special Interest Model Books Ltd.
P.O.Box 327
Poole
Dorset
BH15 2RG
England

First published by Argus Books 1986
Reprinted 1994

This edition published by Special Interest Model Books Ltd. 2005

Reprinted 2013

The right of Ian Bradley to be identified as the Author of this work has been asserted by him in accordance with the Copyright, Designs and Patents Rights Act of 1988.

ISBN 0-85242-887-1

www.specialinterestmodelbooks.co.uk

Printed and bound in Great Britain by Short Run Press Ltd.

Preface

The saw is not only one of the oldest
but perhaps one of the most important
tools in the craftsman's armoury. It
is also, without doubt, one that has
suffered a great deal of abuse over
the years.

The author, therefore, makes no
apology for introducing a book designed
to cover the whole subject as widely as
possible, within the limits of available
space of course, and to include in it
some practical notes on the use of both
hand and machine saws.

In its preparation the following firms
have provided information and illustrations: Messrs. James Neill Limited of
Sheffield, Wadkin Limited of Leicester,
W. J. Meddings Limited of Ivybridge,
Devon, Black and Decker of Maidenhead
and Peter Gee of Dereham, Norfolk.

Their valuable and welcome assist-
ance is hereby gratefully acknowledged.

I.B.   Hungerford 1986

Contents

PART 1
CHAPTER 1

The Wood Saw

The saw, in its various forms, is one of the oldest tools in the workman's armoury. Without it one would find it difficult to visualise how any work could be initiated.

Essentially the saw consists of a blade having teeth formed on one edge.

In the past a variety of objects has been used to provide the cutting edge; these differ from sharks' teeth – set in a wooden blade – to precious stones let into a bronze matrix. The former is said to have been used by the South American Indians, while the Egyptians

Fig. 1A *Two saws from Western Australia. (a) Inserted stone plates, (b) Inserted glass plates*

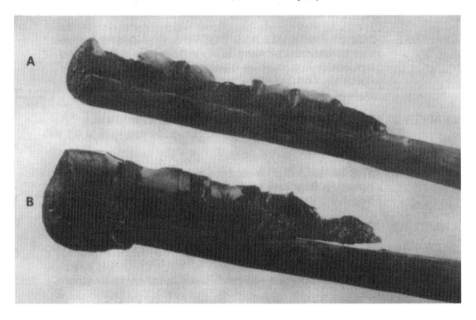

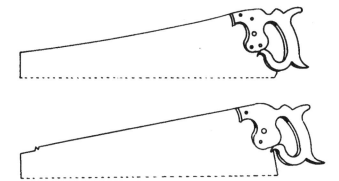

Fig.1 *The skew-backed saw.*

Fig. 2 *The straight-backed saw.*

are said to have used the latter combination to cut granite and metal, presumably when building the Pyramids and other architectural works.

The two saws in Fig. 1(a) come from Western Australia. The saw depicted at (a) has inserted stone plates while that at (b) has plates of glass embedded in clay baked to harden it.

So far as woodworking hand-saws are concerned these have developed into two main classes, the cross-cut saw and the rip saw. As these terms should convey, the former is intended for cutting across the grain of the wood while the latter is used for cutting along the grain.

Hand-saws in the past have been made either Skew-back or Straight-back. The first is to be preferred as it is lighter and tends to clear in the 'kerf', that is the cut made by the saw itself, rather more easily than does the straight-back saw.

The two forms of hand-saw are shown in Fig. 1 and Fig. 2. It is sometimes convenient, as an example when sawing logs for firewood, to provide means whereby two operatives can use the saw at the same time. In the case of

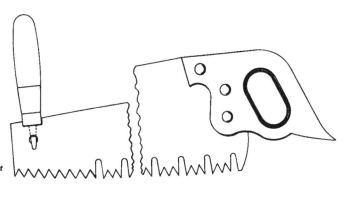

Fig. 3 *The two-handed cross-cut saw.*

9

Fig. 4 *Pit-saw equipment from the mid-18th century.*

a medium-sized cross-cut saw this is achieved by attaching an upright handle to the leading end of the blade as depicted in Fig. 3.

The saw blade has a hole punched in it and a threaded hook is inserted in this hole and pulled up tight by means of the handle which is turned to impart the necessary tension.

The two-handed saw is, of course, by no means a modern conception, for it was the standard method once used when ripping down long timbers in days gone by.

Fig. 4 demonstrates the equipment used by sawyers about 1750. The saws, some of which may be seen hanging up, were provided with cross handles at each end of the blade. In use one man stood on the timber to be sawn while the second, his mate, took his place below in the pit. Sawing was performed by each man in turn pulling the saw towards him, upwards by the man on top and downwards by the sawyer below. Meanwhile wedges were driven into the saw kerf to ensure that the timber did not bind on the saw blade.

The saw pit itself was straddled by a pair of heavy timbers while the work was supported on ties which bridged those timbers.

10

Fig. 5

Fig. 6

Fig. 7

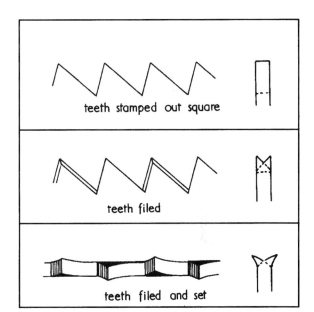

teeth stamped out square

teeth filed

teeth filed and set

Stages in forming saw teeth.

In passing it is perhaps worth noting that all two-handed sawing is carried out by *pulling* the saw, not pushing it, as anyone cutting firewood by this method will have found out.

Some good examples of pit saws are to be found in the Folk Museum near Aberystwyth, Wales, where many of the tools used by the old craftsmen are to be found.

Hand-saw Teeth
The teeth of the hand-saw are just stamped out of the edge of the blade square with its axis; they are then filed and set in order to give clearance to the saw when in use. These stages are depicted in Figs. 5, 6 and 7.

The angularity of the teeth depends upon the use to which the saw is to be put, that is to say whether the saw is to be used for crosscutting or for ripping. These variations are depicted in Fig. 8.

There are four main variations of saw tooth pattern in use for hand-saws. Of these we have already taken note of the patterns commonly applied to hand-saws used for cross-cutting and ripping. There are, however, two further patterns that have been found in connection with two-handed saws. The first of these is shown at (a) in Fig. 9.

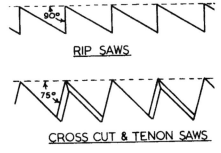

RIP SAWS

CROSS CUT & TENON SAWS

Fig. 8 *Variations in sawtooth angle.*

11

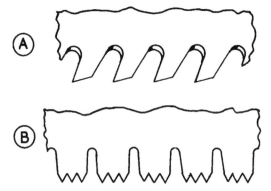

Fig. 9 *Saw tooth patterns for two-handed saws.*

This is the gullet-tooth once used with pit-saws for cutting along the grain of the wood.

The Encyclopaedia Britannica describes the gullet-tooth in the following terms: 'The rationale of the gullet-tooth is clear, the keen chisel-like edges of the teeth being well adapted for slicing the fibres of the wood transversely, and for this it leaves little to be desired'.

Forms of Hand-saw

We have already noticed the pit-saw, sometimes called the whip-saw in old books, and the hand-saw which is some 26″ long and intended to be used by a single man. There are a number of other forms of saw for hand use, however, that need to be mentioned.

1. **The Panel Saw** is about the same length as the hand-saw but the blade is thinner and the pitching of the saw teeth much closer.

2. **The Bow or Frame Saw** depicted in Fig. 10 is of some antiquity and has now seemingly fallen into disuse, though examples are sometimes to be found.

3. **The Tenon Saw** is used for cutting across the fibres of wood, that is across the grain, getting its name from its employment in forming the shoulders of wood tenons.

4. **The Compass Saw** Fig. 11 and Fig. 12 is used for cutting circular or irregular curved work. As distinct from other forms of saw the teeth are not set,

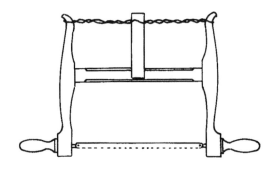

Fig. 10 *The bow or frame saw.*

Fig. 11 *The compass saw, also sometimes called a pad-saw.*

Fig. 12 *Compass saw with three blades.*

Fig. 13 *Key-hole saw, also known as a pad-saw.*

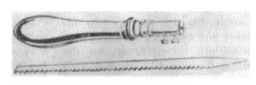

Fig. 14 *Iron-handled pad-saw.*

since were they set the saw would tend to keep a straight line and so be difficult to operate.

5. **The Key-hole Saw,** sometimes called the pad-saw, Fig. 13 and Fig. 14, as its name implies is a form of compass-saw intended for cutting sharp curves such as keyholes themselves. The handle is long and is perforated throughout its length, so that the saw blade can be set at any desired distance within the handle where it is secured by a set-screw. The blade is long and narrow, consequently, in order to preserve rigidity, only the shortest amount of blade that is sufficient for the work is allowed to project from the handle. It is perhaps worth noting that this type of tool is often called a pad-saw.

Sharpening Saws

Sharp tools are the prerequisite for good work and saws are no exception. The procedure for carrying out the sharpening is quite simple, if a trifle time-consuming; however, providing the matter is treated methodically success can be assured.

In the previous chapter we have considered the difference between the rip saw and the cross-cut saw, and the variation in tooth form and angle in both cases, so while sharpening a saw it is, of course, necessary to preserve these essentials.

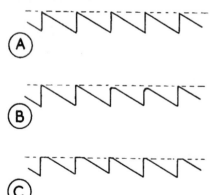

Fig. 1 *Topping saw teeth.*

A saw may become blunted for a variety of reasons and amongst them may well be accidental contact between hidden nails and the saw teeth. Be that as it may, general wear results in the tops of the saw teeth coming out of line. The first step, therefore, is to restore this alignment.

In order to do so the crests of the saw teeth will need to be 'topped' in order that those teeth that are high are reduced to a common level.

Fig. 1 depicts the three stages that concern the first part of the re-sharpening process. At A the ideal state of the saw teeth is represented, for all the crests are level with the broken line. When wear has taken place some of the teeth may have worn down below the line as at B. It will be necessary therefore to file down the high teeth till their tops are level with those seen below the dotted line; this condition is seen represented at C.

It is, of course, important that the filing should be quite square with the side of the saw blade. To ensure this, the file to be used should be clamped to a square piece of timber about 10-12″ long, which, when placed against the side of the saw, will not only make certain that the file is applied squarely but that it is travelling in a straight line up and down the tops of the saw teeth.

Whilst it may suffice to secure the file by a pair of G-clamps as a temporary measure, when much sharpening needs to be done it may pay to make a simple wood fixture, such as that depicted in Fig. 2, which will not only hold the file firmly but will be found rather more comfortable to use.

Two clamps are needed, one at each end of the file; as will be seen, the clamps are secured to the block by woodscrews.

Sharpening the Saw Teeth

Once the saw teeth have been topped they have to be sharpened by a filing operation.

The files used for the purpose are triangular and, for the most part, are double ended. In the case of the rip saw the file is applied to the teeth at right angles to the axis of the saw blade itself, while when sharpening a cross-cut saw the file is held at an angle to the axis.

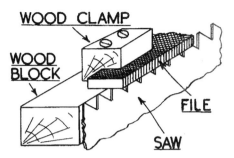

Fig. 2 *Simple device for "topping" saw teeth.*

When filing the teeth, the blade must be gripped between two pieces of board set in the vice. These will keep the saw blade straight and clamp out the inevitable screeching sound produced by the filing operation. For this reason the saw teeth should be allowed to project from the pieces of board a short distance only as shown in Fig. 3.

Once the teeth of the saw have been filed to shape they have to be set, in order to ensure clearance to the blade during the saw operation.

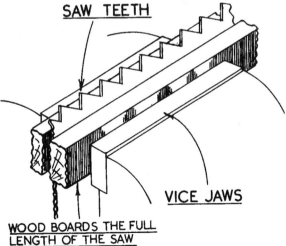

Fig. 3 *Holding the saw for filing the teeth.*

Fig. 4 *A simple saw set.*

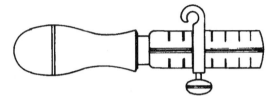

Fig. 5 *Notched saw set with gauge.*

Setting the Saw Teeth

Setting the teeth involves bending alternate teeth outward in opposite directions. This operation needs to be carried out with some care, bending each tooth evenly so far as is possible. There are several forms of saw-set, the simplest of which is shown in Fig. 4. This is

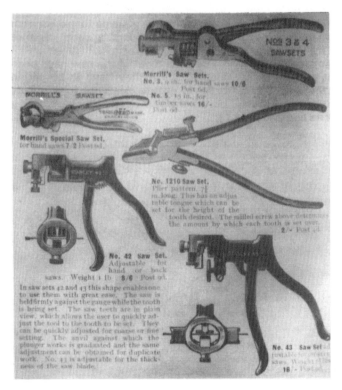

Fig. 6 *Plunger type saw sets from an early catalogue.*

a notched blade fitted with a handle to give adequate leverage during the setting process. The notches, as may be noticed, are of different widths to suit the varying thickness of saw blades in use. With such a simple device the amount of set is left to the judgement of the operator, as indeed is its evenness as between successive teeth.

For this reason the simple saw-set is provided with a gauge which can be adjusted to suit the notch in use. The gauge is so adjusted that, when the tooth is bent outwards sufficiently, the gauge will touch the side of the saw blade. A notched saw set with gauge is depicted in Fig. 5.

The professional worker and the experienced amateur now largely make use of plunger saw-sets of the type shown in Fig. 6. With this type of set, for the most part, a plunger is pressed against the saw teeth when the handles are squeezed together; when the handles are released the plunger springs back. Naturally means are provided for adjusting the saw-sets to suit the various sizes of saw available.

The illustration reproduced is of a page taken from the catalogue of the late George Adams of High Holborn, London, who will doubtless be remembered by older readers for the quality and variety of the tools he kept in stock in his London shop.

The Saw-setting Block
The oldest method of setting the teeth of a saw is to place the blade on a cast iron or hard wood block having a bevelled edge. The teeth are set to project over the bevel and are then hit with a hammer in order to bend them to the correct angle. In the hands of an expert this is probably the most rapid way of setting the teeth. A special saw-

Fig. 7 *Saw-setting blocks and hammer.*

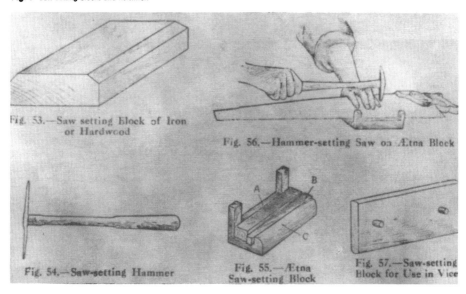

Fig. 53.—Saw setting block of Iron or Hardwood

Fig. 56.—Hammer-setting Saw on Ætna Block

Fig. 54.—Saw-setting Hammer

Fig. 55.—Ætna Saw-setting Block

Fig. 57.—Saw-setting Block for Use in Vice

Fig. 8. *The "Eclipse" No. 77 saw set.*

setting hammer is required for the work as may be deduced from Fig. 7.

This illustration, which is taken with acknowledgements from 'The Practical Woodworker', demonstrates various aspects of the setting block and its use.

The setting block is about 7 or 8" long with its upper edges bevelled as shown. The bevelled edges each have a different slope so that they will serve for varying sizes of teeth. In use the saw is held flat on the block with its teeth projecting over the bevel. Each alternate tooth is then struck with the hammer. The saw is then turned over and the process repeated.

The Ætna saw setting block depicted is an iron casting in which A is a steel block with its edges bevelled at varying angles and B is a steel wedge to hold the block in place in the casting C. The method of using this saw setting device is also seen in the illustration.

Alternatively, an ordinary hammer and a nail punch may be used together with the setting-block, which may well be made from hard wood if the work is to be carried out by amateur hands.

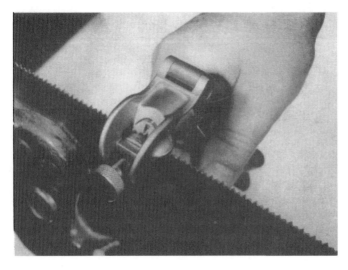

Fig. 9 *The "Eclipse" saw set in use.*

The Eclipse No. 77 Saw Sets

The saw set in Fig. 8 is a product of James Neill of Sheffield, England. It is designed specifically for use with *hand-saws* and is seen in operation in Fig. 9.

There are, of course, several points to watch when using this type of saw set and in this connection the makers of the 'Eclipse' saw set have put together a leaflet in several languages, the English version of which is reproduced below.

A number of warnings are given and of these two perhaps are pre-eminently important:

The first, to make sure that the saw to be serviced is made of a material that can be set; some modern saw blades are expendable.

The second, never to reverse the set of a saw tooth (one supposes this could happen accidentally) – reversal might easily break a tooth.

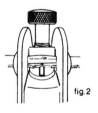

Instructions for use
Not for circular saws

For handsaws, 4 to 12 points/inch (25mm), maximum thickness 16 S.W.G. – 1.6mm.
The anvil numbers correspond with the numbers of points/inch.
In use, the hammer presses the tooth against the anvil.
Designed so that set does not exceed half the tooth depth.

Adjustment
Hold in the normal working position.
Release knurled anvil screw, press and turn until appropriate anvil number is in line with the hammer (fig. 1).
Compress handles to grip the anvil.
Tighten the knurled anvil screw.

Choice of Anvil Number
Do not adhere rigidly to the points numbers. Be guided by experience, to suit the wood to be cut and the hardness of the saw teeth.
When setting teeth on extra hard saws, adjust the anvil one number higher than the saw points number.
Some modern saws are expendible; longer life than more ordinary saws but never to be serviced. Because of the risk of tooth breakage, it may be dangerous to attempt to set the teeth on such saws.
Check the adjustment by trial setting of teeth at the handle end of the saw.

Using the saw set
Always follow the saw makers instructions.
Hold the saw in a vice.
Place the head of the Saw Set over the saw, so that the tooth to be set is directly in line with the hammer (fig. 2).
NEVER reverse the set of a tooth.
AVOID all change in the relative positions of saw and Saw Set.
AVOID excessive pressure.
AVOID leverage or twisting.
Just squeeze the handles together gently, and let the Saw Set do the work.
Then release the handles, and lift the Saw Set clear before moving it to the next tooth.

Fig. 10 *Instructions for using the saw set.*

19

PART 1
CHAPTER 3

The Circular Saw

Once the amateur or the small professional woodworking shop has decided to mechanise the plant, and to go in for power-driven tools, probably the first machine to be purchased will be a circular saw. In this way not only will a lot of fatigue be avoided but the quality of the workmanship may be much enhanced. For the most part woodworking tools are somewhat power-consuming though it is quite surprising what a lot of work can be carried out by means of the saw attachments provided by the makers of electric hand drills.

The history of the circular saw is somewhat obscure. But the Encyclopaedia Britannica attributes its origin to Brunel who used it first in 1790 when it formed part of the block-making machinery he was setting up in Portsmouth Dockyard. This equipment has been the subject of a booklet published by H.M. Stationery Office, Kingsway, London.

Fig. 1 *Brunel's Pendulum Saw.*

Fig. 2 *An old-time circular saw bench.*

From this monograph, 'The Portsmouth Blockmaking Machinery', it would seem that the real inventor of the circular saw was one Walter Taylor, the head of Taylor's of Southampton who, until Brunel and his special equipment came on the scene, were the principal suppliers of blocks to the Admiralty.

Brunel's first application of the device, if not the only one, was in the pendulum saw; this machine was hung from the rafters of the workshop in a frame capable of being swung to-and-fro so that timber placed on a table in its orbit could be cross-cut to lengths suited to the making of the blocks that were to be produced.

Brunel's pendulum saw is depicted in Fig. 1. It would appear that Brunel called on his experience with the contemporary centre lathe when designing the bearing arrangements for his saw spindle. The mandrels of centre lathes made about this time were carried in a reversed-cone bearing at the forward end, while at the opposite end the mandrel was seated in a plain journal. In order to take care of end float, and to maintain adjustment of the forward bearing, an axial screw was fitted in an attachment at the rear of the plain bearing. In the case of Brunel's pendulum saw a similar arrangement can be seen in the bearing assembly nearest the camera.

Somewhat the same arrangement would appear to apply to the circular saw bench in Fig. 2. But here, however, the spindle was mounted on centres at each end which could only be adjusted to take up shake when it occurred. One would imagine that this could be pretty often, the more so if the saw bench was being roughly handled. The illustration reproduced here appears in a book entitled 'Arts and Sciences' published about 1800, so it may be that the representation of this circular saw bench is more diagrammatic than factual. However, it is very probable that the basic design indicated is accurate. There would seem to be little versatility in such a machine, which could do little more than act as a rip saw for cutting down lengths of timber.

At the turn of the century a number of amateur workers' wood-turning lathes were adapted to circular sawing. For the most part the saws were 6" diameter, mounted on arbors set between centres in the lathe, and driven from the mandrel catch plate through a carrier on the saw arbor.

An example belonging to a relative of the author was used in high-class cabinet-making for many years. This device comprised a wooden box mounted on the lathe bed, and having a hinged top that could be adjusted to set the depth of cut required.

Two saws were provided, each mounted on a separate arbor, one for ripping, the other for cross-cutting. The arrangement is depicted diagrammatically in Fig. 2(a). Some lathe manufacturers at the present time have adopted similar devices as attachments for their products. It must be remem-

bered, however, that the average amateur metal-turning lathe is not well adapted to wood sawing because of its low spindle speed.

Some 30 or 40 years ago there was on the market a number of well-designed light circular saw benches very suitable for use by the amateur or the small professional workshop. Some of these machines were treadle driven while others were intended to be mounted on the bench and driven by electric motors set below it. All the best of these machines had rise and fall tables, and a great many of them were provided with ball-bearing plummer blocks for the saw spindle, though, it must be added, those with plain bearings gave equally good service when the design and the fitting was of a high standard.

Fences for ripping and cross-cutting were supplied and it was common for the cross-cutting fence to be capable of angular setting so that mitre sawing could be undertaken.

The saw benches in Fig. 3 and Fig. 4 are typical of the equipment to which reference has been made. The former is a bench once supplied by the late George Adams whose reputation for marketing high grade tools of all types

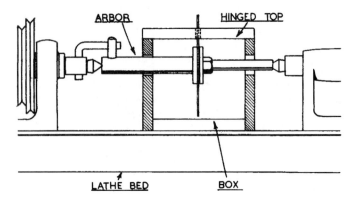

Fig. 2A *Saw adaptation for a wood turning lathe.*

SAW BENCHES

will be remembered by many and particularly by those of the same age group as the author.

Fig. 3 (left) *The George Adams saw bench.*
Fig. 4 (above) *An American small saw bench.*

The second saw bench is an American-made machine imported about 35 years ago by E. P. Barrus, who specialised in tools and equipment from the U.S.A. The machine illustrated was intended for driving by V-rope, whilst the George Adams saw bench, as befits the age in which it was produced, had a flat belt drive.

Both machines were fitted with guards over the saw itself, a requirement the desirability of which cannot be too strongly emphasised.

Fig. 5 *The Black and Decker portable saw.*

Fig. 6 *The Black and Decker saw bench.*

Sawing Attachments for the Electric Hand Drill

Of late years the do-it-yourself handyman has demanded and been supplied with sawing attachments for various makes of electric hand drill on the market.

The range of equipment manufactured by Black and Decker of Maidenhead serves well to demonstrate the facilities available. For the most part the devices to be described are attachments to be made to an electric hand drill though some may be obtained as individual or independent machines.

The Portable Saw Attachment D.7876

This attachment is in Fig. 5. It is fully adjustable for angle as well as for depth of cut. A fence is provided that enables accurate rip-sawing to be carried out.

Portable Saw Bench D.1660

The portable saw bench depicted in Fig. 5 may be mounted under the saw bench in Fig. 6. As has already been said, the attachment is adjustable for both angle and depth of cut so the saw bench also has these facilities. The bench also has a graduated protractor for mitre-cutting and an adjustable fence for rip-sawing.

The author has made some additions and modifications to the saw bench. In the main these comprise extension platforms at each end of the original bench in order to enable relatively long pieces of wood to be rip-sawed more easily. At the same time the framework of the original bench was walled in on three sides, with a flexible covering on the fourth side, in order to retain the sawdust produced during the sawing process. The arrangement is depicted diagrammatically in Fig. 6(a).

The right-hand extension is made to fold down. This enables the set-up to be shortened for packing away in the shop.

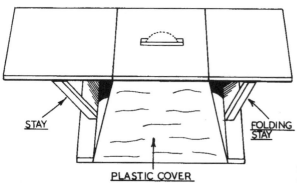

STAY

FOLDING STAY

PLASTIC COVER

Fig. 6A *The author's modification to the Black and Decker saw bench.*

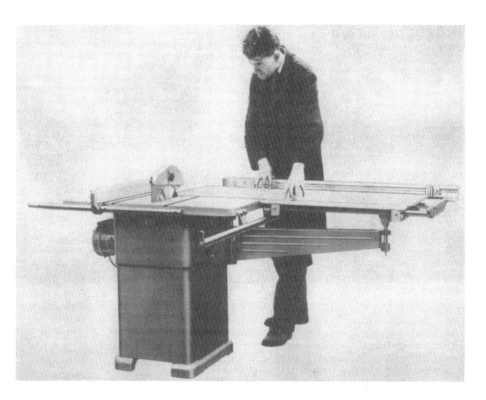

Fig. 7 *The Wadkin Bursgreen 10 inch saw bench.*

In the original saw bench the gap in which the saw itself operates is wide, otherwise it would be impossible to tilt the saw for cutting on the angle. The gap has now been restricted by the insertion of a wooden filling piece in which the saw was allowed to cut its own clear way by the simple process of operating the cleating arrangement whilst the saw is actually rotating.

The filling piece can, of course, be removed if angular cutting has to be undertaken.

The Jigsaw Attachment W.1017

This is a most useful fitment that is attached directly to the electric drill, although the tool has proved so useful that several manufacturers market complete jigsaws or 'sabre saws'. The device is eminently suitable for contour-sawing in wood, metal and plastics. The author has used the equipment on a number of occasions when other methods would have been of little avail.

The Wadkin 10″ Sawbench

The sawbench in Fig. 7 is a good example of modern professional equipment. It is fitted with a 10″ (250m/m) saw carried on a ⅝″ arbor. Such a machine is in every way a versatile saw-

25

CIRCULAR SAWS

BS 96
A general purpose
RIP SAW
for hard or soft woods

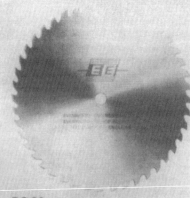

BS 97
For CROSS
CUTTING or
RIPPING with an
exceptionally smooth
finish.
BS 100 as above but
HOLLOW GROUND

BS 98
A general purpose
CROSS CUT SAW

BS 96
This is our standard range of saws,
normally available from stock. Hollow
ground saws require no setting, give
minimum saw kerf or wastage and
ensure exceptionally clean finish.

bench, being capable of compound angle crosscutting and bevel ripping with the saw itself canted. In the illustration the bench is seen with the sliding extension table set up. By this means cross-cutting or ripping on large panels can be undertaken.

When angular ripping or compound angular crosscutting has to be undertaken the arbor can be tilted to allow the saw itself to assume the angle desired.

The Circular Saw
The various types of saw that are commonly used appear in Fig. 8, and it will be noticed that in some instances they may be obtained in hollow ground form. Saws made in this way need no setting; consequently the saw kerf is kept to a minimum with the resultant greatly reduced wastage of wood when expensive timber is being sawn.

Mechanical Pit Saws
The particular saw seen in Fig. 9 is a single-bladed machine for cutting up or squaring logs. It dates from 1902 and it was designed to deal with oak timbers from 12" to 28" in depth, when it had a rate of feed from 8" to 4" a minute.

The machine depicted is, of course, a model, which may be seen in the Science Museum. As may be surmised, the upper platform represents the floor of the sawmill with the drive to the saw frame mounted below; the frame is carried in guides machined in a heavy iron casting forming part of the main machine assembly. The log to be sawn is mounted on a travelling carriage driven through a rack and pinion from the mechanism seen to the left of the illustration. An interesting feature of the general design is the setting of the saw blade out of the vertical in relation to the longitudinal axis of the work. In this way the teeth of the saw do not drag through the work on the upper or non-working stroke.

27

PART 1
CHAPTER 4

Using Wood Saws

In the space of a single chapter one can only hope to deal cursorily with the subject of sawing wood by hand. For the most part this is confined to ripping and cross-cutting with a hand-saw and to cross-cutting with the tenon saw.

In the amateur and small workshop rip-sawing is performed with a circular saw, whilst the tenon saw is used for cross-cutting, in the main for bench work. The work is either held in the vice or secured against a simple device called the bench hook.

The Bench Hook

Bench hooks are made in two forms; a simple device such as in Fig. 1(a) and a larger and more versatile form in Fig. 1(b).

Both forms of bench hook are built up from odd pieces of timber, sawed and glued together. The first is often used in pairs whilst the larger sees service with cabinet-makers and those dealing with small components on the bench.

As may be inferred bench hooks are placed on the work bench so that their outer ends overhang its edge, as in Fig. 2.

As has already been mentioned, the bench hook is used, for the most part, where working with the tenon saw, so it may not be out of place to draw attention to the correct method of using this type of saw.

First then, when starting a cut the saw should commence working at the side of the work farthest away from the operator. As the cut proceeds the saw is gradually lowered until a kerf is formed

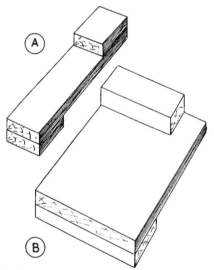

Fig. 1 *Bench Hooks.*

parallel with the surface of the work. This procedure is depicted diagrammatically in Fig. 3.

If the larger of the two bench hooks illustrated is in use its extended floor will give support to the work that will permit the saw to break through cleanly, though it may be advisable to provide some additional support when the work overhangs the bench hook to any extent.

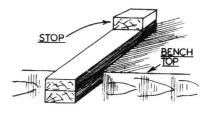

Fig. 2 *The place of the bench hook on the bench.*

When holding work in the bench vice the same procedure must be followed when starting the sawcut.

The tenon saw is used, for the most part, in cross-cutting; but it can, of course, be employed for sawing along the grain, though necessarily to a limited extent.

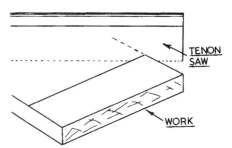

Fig. 3 *Starting the Tenon Saw.*

Sawing Along the Grain

Earlier in the book we have referred to the rip saw which is the correct tool for sawing along the grain. Short pieces of wood are held in the bench vice for ripping while long lengths are mounted on the sawing horse, or between a pair of horses, for the purpose.

The sawing horse will be familiar to many readers. It consists of a couple of A-frame leg assemblies surmounted by a spine that holds them together. The woodworker uses these supports whenever long material needs to be handled.

The sawing horse is depicted in Fig. 4.

The horse needs to be made from substantial material and well stayed so that it remains rigid at all times.

When starting the sawcut, the worker, having lined out the work with a pencil as a guide, rests the saw blade against his left thumb. In this way the teeth can be made to enage the pencil line correctly and the sawing operation can then proceed.

At first the work is set against a single horse but later, when the sawing has proceeded a little way, say for a couple of feet or so, the board is supported on a pair of horses with the second of these as close to the point of sawing as possible. As the sawing proceeds the

Fig. 4 *The Sawing Horse.*

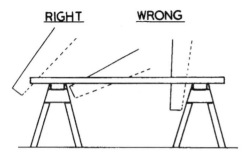

RIGHT   WRONG

Fig. 5 *Correct and incorrect angles for rip-sawing.*

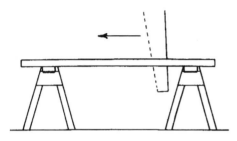

Fig. 6 *The cabinet-makers method of rip-sawing.*

horse is moved along to continue the support.

The angle at which the saw blade meets the work is important. This point is depicted diagrammatically in Fig. 5. As will be seen the optimum angle of attack is about 60 degrees to the work. If the saw is held too flat or too upright sawing becomes tedious.

For the most part the workman makes the sawcut in a direction towards himself; however, some cabinet-makers in the past have used a procedure in which the saw is held vertically, with the teeth *away* from the operator and is pushed along the sawcut with the saw itself angled some 10-15 degrees from the vertical in the direction of the saw cut as depicted in Fig. 6.

The operation needs both hands to be gripping the handle. For this reason the sawyer stands to the side of the work and not above it as in normal practice. The direction of the cut is as indicated in the sketch.

PART 1
APPENDIX

Stone Sawing

Saws for the cutting of stone have been mentioned earlier in this book, as have some of the media used for the purpose. In the past plain iron blades without teeth have been used. These were reciprocated in the stone using abrasive grains suspended in water to carry out the actual cutting. Those readers who have either drilled, or seen glass drilled with a copper tube and emery or carbo-

rundum powder, using turpentine as a lubricant, will understand the method.

Fig. 1, which is reproduced from Leonardo da Vinci's sketch book, shows an arrangement for cutting stone using the technique described above. The machine depicted was intended to be used by one man, though smaller sketches to the left of the illustration reveal an alternative arrangement allowing two men to operate the device.

To go further back in time, the

Egyptians, when building the Pyramids, made much use of saws when cutting the granite of which their buildings are largely composed. The saws themselves were made of bronze in which were embedded precious stones or pieces of natural corundum. Presumably the sawing was carried out dry; certainly it was accurate, for the errors in the construction of the Pyramids have been shown to be negligible.

The whole subject of working stone is treated exhaustively by Holtzapffel in his 5-volume treatise on mechanical manipulation. Those who would wish to learn more of the subject are advised to consult Volume III of the series. It may be hard to come by, but the Library Service should be able to find a copy.

Modern Practice in Stone Sawing

The methods outlined previously are, of course, somewhat time-consuming and unacceptable industrially. For this reason modern practice is to make use of an abrasive cut-off wheel, sometimes diamond impregnated, and to run it at speeds of from 4000 to 8000 surface feet per minute, suiting the characteristics of the wheel to the material to be cut. In this way granite, marble and slate are regularly cut together with other natural and artificial stones.

The use of diamond-mounted cut-off wheels may seem to many a very modern technique, but Holtzapffel has shown that in the stone-working trade they appear to have been commonplace in the middle of the 19th century.

Fig. 1 *Leonardo da Vinci's design for a machine to saw stone.*

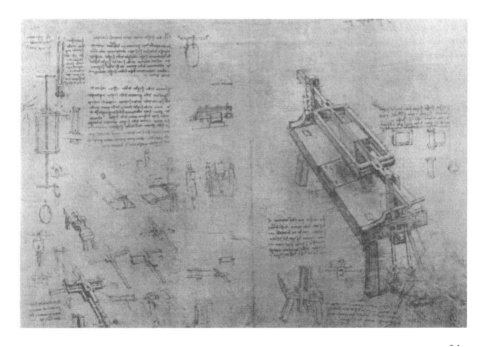

PART 2
CHAPTER 1

The Hacksaw

In the small workshop the hacksaw has many important functions to perform. It is commonly used to cut material to length before machining, to rough-shape parts before a final filing operation and often to remove surplus material in advance of some machining process.

The several manufacturers of saw frames and blades are always willing to supply information on their products, so the newcomer is well advised to seek the authorative advice they are able to give.

The Hacksaw Frame

Originally commercial hacksaw blades were made to a single length, namely 9", so that there was no requirement for anything other than a fixed frame to accommodate them.

A typical frame is shown in Fig. 1(a). It will be seen to consist of a bow, usually of steel though some early examples appear to have had cast-iron bows, and a wooden handle incorporating one anchorage for the saw blade itself. At the opposite end is the other anchorage for the blade, which consisted (and still consists), of a square section member passing through a corresponding square hole in the bow and fitted with a wing

nut to put tension on the blade. The saw blade itself is located by a pin set in each of the anchorages. These pins are usually set at a slight angle with the object of drawing the face of the saw blade into contact with each anchorage, thus helping to preserve the alignment of the blade as a whole.

This minor but important point is depicted in Fig. 1(d).

The five saw frames depicted in Fig. 2A are clearly predecessors of modern practice. Today's method of tensioning the saw blade owes its introduction to the class of saw illustrated, and the whole conception, though for the most

Fig. 1A *Hacksaw frame, fixed.*

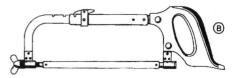

Fig. 1B *Hacksaw frame, adjustable.*

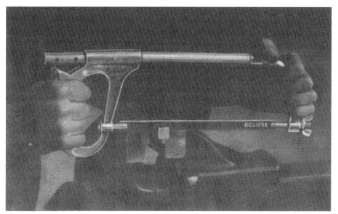

part highly ornamental, is quite modern in appearance. The saws illustrated date from the 17th and 18th centuries.

The group of hacksaws illustrated in the photo Fig. 2B is interesting since it demonstrates how stabilised the basic design of the hacksaw has become during the last two hundred years.

The largest of the saws depicted dates from the 18th century while the saw in the centre of the illustration was made

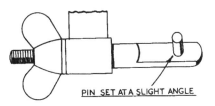

PIN SET AT A SLIGHT ANGLE

Fig. 1D *The blade anchorage and tensioning wing nut.*

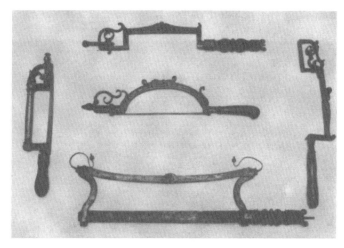

Fig. 2A *Five 16th and 17th Century saws.*

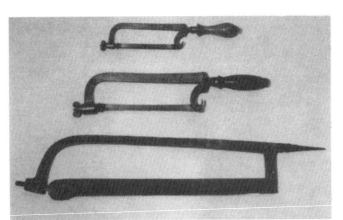

about 1850. The tool at the top of the picture is a hacksaw made by J. Buck, a well-known tool merchant of the time, in 1891.

The somewhat ornate nature of two of the saws will be noted.

Early forms of saw frame had no provision for setting the saw blade at right angles to its normal setting.

In this connection it is sometimes expedient to cut downwards with the saw frame on its side. To do so involves adjusting the position of the blade to allow this to happen; the modern frame has this provision.

A typical example, the product of James Neill & Co., is shown in action in Fig. 3. It will be appreciated that, when using the hacksaw with the blade set in its normal position, the depth of cut is somewhat circumscribed, being controlled by the distance from the saw teeth to the inside of the saw frame. On the other hand when the frame is used on its side there is no limit to the depth of cut but the maximum width of the

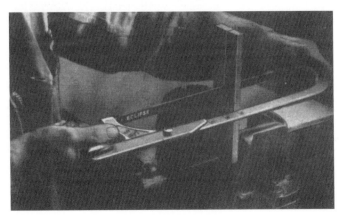

Fig. 3 *Cutting downwards with the saw frame on its side.*

piece cut off is again the distance from the saw teeth to the inside of the frame.

A typical method of ensuring that the saw blade remains in alignment in the frame is depicted in Fig. 4. This is the arrangement adopted by L. S. Starret of America.

As will be seen each frame lug is provided with a pair of V-notches set at right angles to one another. These allow the blade anchorages to be turned 90 degrees and secured by a pin engaging the notch at the handle end, while at the front end of the frame a projection machined on the sleeve against which the wing nut abuts also engages notches formed on the lug. In this way, when rotated, the anchorages remain in true alignment with each other.

The sleeve is fitted with a grub-screw engaging a keyway formed in the anchorage itself. This arrangement prevents the anchorage from turning when the wing nut is moved to put tension on the saw blade.

The Adjustable Hacksaw Frame

Hand hacksaw blades are obtainable in 10″ and 12″ lengths and, in order to accommodate both sizes in one tool, adjustable frames can be provided.

For the most part the method of adjustment consists of making the spine of the frame telescopic and arranging for some detent to lock the frame in whatever position is necessary. Three devices or arrangements designed to do this are depicted in Fig. 5.

Specialised Saw Frames

As might be expected, with the basic design features of the frame stabilised, there are special saw frames available for a number of purposes. For example the saw in Fig. 6 has a deep throated

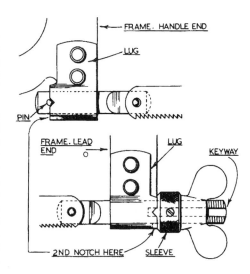

Fig. 4 *L.S. Starret's method of aligning the saw blade.*

frame making it especially suitable for use on rolled steel joists and girders.

The frame in Fig. 7 is one of the Junior saws made by 'Eclipse' to take

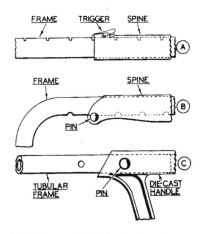

Fig. 5 *Three methods of adjusting the saw frame.*

35

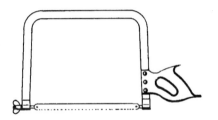

Fig. 6 *The deep-throated saw frame.*

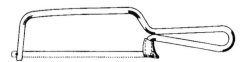

Fig. 7 *The "Eclipse" Junior saw frame.*

The frames depicted in Fig. 8 were produced by the author many years ago to apply a positive adjustable tension to the saw. They have been found very successful for they tend to keep the blade straight, a factor that prolongs the life of the blade.

Fretsaw and Piercing Saw Frames

The fretsaw in Fig. 9 is used, as many readers will know, when it is necessary to saw somewhat intricate carved work. Its deep throat enables the user to encompass quite large surfaces. It can be used on metal and plastics but it is,

their Junior saw blades. These blades are flexible and are designed to cut any material commonly encountered by workers in the various spheres of engineering. The blades are unbreakable in normal use; they cut rapidly and have been found satisfactory when used in a light power hacksaw made by the author.

The two Junior saw frames from 'Eclipse' have, in one instance, a pre-set blade tension; in the other a limited tension is applied to the blade when the handle is turned to secure the saw itself.

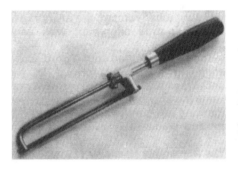

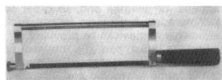

Fig. 8 *The author's saw frames for Junior blades.*

perhaps, most useful in the woodworking field.

The special blades needed when using the fretsaw will be discussed later.

The piercing saw, seen in Fig. 10, is intended for fine work in all metals and is commonly used by silversmiths and goldsmiths.

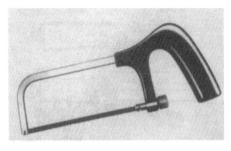

Fig. 7A *The "Eclipse" No. 675 saw frame.*

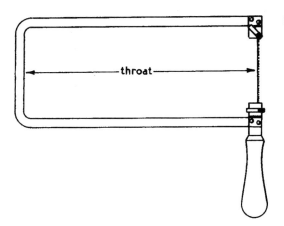

Fig. 9 *The Fretsaw.*

throat

Fig. 10 *The Piercing saw.*

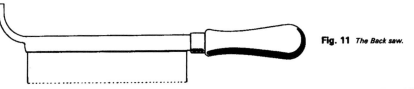

Fig. 11 *The Back saw.*

The Back Saw

Finally we must take note of the back saw depicted in Fig. 11. As illustrated the saw has a non-detachable blade, but modern versions of the tool now have detachable and alternative blades enabling them to be used in a variety of circumstances. The saw is somewhat like the carpenter's tenon saw, having a rigid back to give it strength while the thumb rest at the front or leading end of the tool helps to promote accuracy when sawing.

Three blades are usually provided, all 5" long, with thicknesses .014", .011" and .008" and having 32, 44 and 60 teeth respectively. The first blade is intended for wood or metal while the other two are most suitable for fine work in metal.

The Hacksaw Blade

One manufacturer has said that the hacksaw blade is very likely the most abused of tools and experience has shown that there is much to justify this view. Later in the book, therefore, we shall be considering measures that will enable the user to get the most out of what is now a comparatively expensive piece of equipment.

Hacksaw blades are either made from High Speed Steel or from Low Alloy Steel. The former gives the best performance, for blades made from this material will cut the harder and tougher materials faster and for a greater length of time than will blades of Low Alloy Steel. These are lower priced and are designed to saw mild steel and the softer metals.

Both types are obtainable in the 'all-hard' condition, a form preferred by experienced workers. On the other hand the flexible form is intended for the less experienced man who, because of the difficult nature of the work, is more liable to break the all-hard blade.

The tables which follow are intended to show the reader what blades are available and to provide him with data that will enable the correct selection of blade to be made.

HIGH SPEED STEEL HACKSAW BLADES

Single Edge – for Hand and Light Power Use

Length in mm	Width in mm	Thickness in mm	Teeth per 25mm	Pin Hole Dia. mm	Length in inches	Width in inches	Thickness in inches	Teeth per inch
FLEXIBLE TYPE								
250	13	0.65	18, 24, 32	4.0	10	½	0.025	18, 24, 32
300	13	0.65	14, 18, 24, 32	4.0	12	½	0.025	14, 18, 24, 32
ALL HARD TYPE								
250	13	0.65	18, 24, 32	4.0	10	½	0.025	18, 24, 32
300	13	0.65	14, 18, 24, 32	4.0	12	½	0.025	14, 18, 24, 32
300	16	0.8	14, 18, 24	5.0	12	⅝	0.032	14, 18, 24

Single Edge – for Power Use

Length in mm	Width in mm	Thickness in mm	Teeth per 25mm	Pin Hole Dia. mm	Length in inches	Width in inches	Thickness in inches	Teeth per inch
300	25	1.25	10, 14	7.0	12	1	0.050	10, 14
350	25	1.25	10, 14	7.0	14	1	0.050	10, 14
350	32	1.6	6, 10	8.5	14	1¼	0.062	6, 10
350	40	2.0	4, 6	10.5	14	1½	0.075	4, 6
400	32	1.6	6, 10	8.5	16	1¼	0.062	6, 10
400	40	2.0	4, 6	10.5	16	1½	0.075	4, 6
425	25	1.25	10, 14	7.0	17	1	0.050	10, 14
425	32	1.6	4, 6, 10	8.5	17	1¼	0.062	4, 6, 10
450	32	1.6	6, 10	8.5	18	1¼	0.062	6, 10
450	40	2.0	4, 6	10.5	18	1½	0.075	4, 6
450	45	2.25	4, 6	10.5	18	1¾	0.088	4, 6
525	40	2.0	6	10.5	21	1½	0.075	6
525	45	2.25	4, 6	10.5	21	1¾	0.088	4, 6
600	45	2.25	4, 6	10.5	24	1¾	0.088	4, 6
600	50	2.5	4, 6	12.5	24	2	0.100	4, 6
750	63	2.5	4	12.5	30	2½	0.100	4

LOW ALLOY STEEL HACKSAW BLADES

Single Edge – for Hand and Light Power Use

Length in mm	Width in mm	Thickness in mm	Teeth per 25mm	Pin Hole Dia. mm	Length in inches	Width in inches	Thickness in inches	Teeth per inch
FLEXIBLE TYPE								
250	13	0.65	18, 24, 32	4.0	10	½	0.025	18, 24, 32
300	13	0.65	14, 18, 24, 32	4.0	12	½	0.025	14, 18, 24, 32
300	16	0.8	14, 18, 24	5.0	12	⅝	0.032	14, 18, 24
ALL HARD TYPE								
250	13	0.65	18, 24, 32	4.0	10	½	0.025	18, 24, 32
300	13	0.65	14, 18, 24, 32	4.0	12	½	0.025	14, 18, 24, 32
300	16	0.8	14, 18, 24	5.0	12	⅝	0.032	14, 18, 24

Double Edge – for Hand Use

Length in mm	Width in mm	Thickness in mm	Teeth per 25mm	To take pin Dia. mm	Length in inches	Width in inches	Thickness in inches	Teeth per inch
250	25	0.8	24	5.0	10	1	0.032	24
300	25	0.8	24	5.0	12	1	0.032	24

Single Edge – for Power Use

Length in mm	Width in mm	Thickness in mm	Teeth per 25mm	Pin Hole Dia. mm	Length in inches	Width in inches	Thickness in inches	Teeth per inch
300	25	1.25	10, 14	7.0	12	1	0.050	10, 14
350	25	1.25	10, 14	7.0	14	1	0.050	10, 14
350	32	1.6	10	8.5	14	1¼	0.062	10
400	25	1.25	10, 14	7.0	16	1	0.050	10, 14
400	32	1.6	10	8.5	16	1¼	0.062	10

It should be noted that normal metric lengths of saw blade are measured between their pin hole centres, while the inch lengths are taken over the outside of the pin holes as seen in Fig. 1.

The reader will have noted the variation in tooth pitch that is available in connection with the various blade lengths listed. The newcomer, therefore, may well be in some difficulty in deciding which pitch is suited to the work in hand.

In general one may summarise the requirements as follows:

1. When cutting soft materials a coarse tooth should be used. Otherwise the teeth will become clogged and the sawing operation will be slowed down.

2. On the other hand if sawing hard materials one should fit a fine-tooth saw, since there is little or no chance of clogging when hard material is being cut.

3. When cutting thin sections, angle and T-section for example, the tooth pitch must not be such that two consecutive teeth straddle the work. Always make sure that at least three consecutive teeth are in contact with the work.

These requirements apply equally well, of course, whether it is a hand-saw or a machine that is being used.

As a guide to the tooth pitch that should be used for a given thickness of material the accompanying table may be of service:

HAND BLADES

Material Thickness Inches	mm	Hard Materials	Soft Materials
Up to ⅛"	Up to 3	32	32
⅛" to ¼"	3 to 6	24	24
¼" to ½"	6 to 13	24	18
½" to 1"	13 to 25	18	14

POWER BLADES

Material Thickness Inches	mm	Hard Materials	Soft Materials
1" to 2"	25 to 50	14	10
2" to 4"	50 to 102	10	6
Over 4"	Over 102	6	4

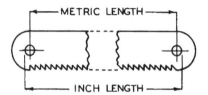

Fig. 1 *Comparison of inch and metric blade.*

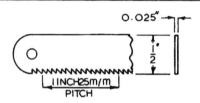

Fig. 2 *Components of the hacksaw blade.*

The dimensional components of the hacksaw blade are shown in Fig. 2. It should be appreciated that, unless some means are taken to prevent it, the saw blade will be liable to jam or stick in the kerf sawn in the work. To avoid this the teeth of the blade are 'set' as depicted in the diagram Fig. 3. Alternate teeth, or a series of alternate teeth, are bent at a slight angle to the axis of the blade, with the effect that the sawn kerf is wider than the thickness of the blade itself. Thus the possibility of metal particles jamming the blade is negatived.

Eclipse Junior Saw Blades,
A word must be said here with reference to these blades. They were designed specifically for use with Eclipse Junior frames. They are supplied with pinned ends to fit these frames and, being flexible, they are virtually unbreakable in normal use.

They will cut metal efficiently as well as plastics and many other materials. Their salient dimensions are:

Fig. 3 *The "set" in the saw blade.*

Total Length	Distance between Pin Centres	Width	Thickness	Tooth Pitch
6"	5½"	.025"	.017"	32
150m/m	140m/m	6m/m	.043m/m	

The author has used these blades in both a light power hacksaw and a jigsaw.

The Abrafile
The Abrafile in Fig. 4 is really not a saw at all but is a species of round file that may be mounted in a hacksaw frame, using links supplied for the purpose. By means of the device one may embark on contour drawing since it is possible to steer the cut in any direction with considerable ease.

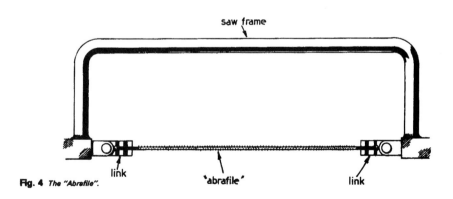

saw frame

Fig. 4 *The "Abrafile".*   link   'abrafile'   link

41

CHAPTER 3

Using the Hand Hacksaw

If the hand hacksaw is to be used accurately and economically there are a number of points that must receive attention.

1. Make sure that the work is gripped firmly in the vice.

2. Check that the saw blade is set square, in abutment with its anchorage and that the teeth are, of course, pointing *away* from the operator! See Fig. 1.

3. Ascertain that the saw blade is correctly tensioned. When fitting a new blade take up the slack with the wing nut then give it three full turns only to apply tension.

When these matters have been satisfactorily attended to the sawing operation may commence.

As depicted in Fig. 2 the cut should always be started on the side of the work away from the operator. When sawing channel, angle or girder sections this is most important, otherwise damage to the saw teeth is likely to occur. The point is illustrated graphically in Fig. 3.

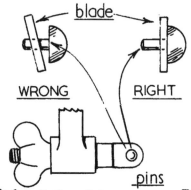

Fig. 1 *Checking the saw blade.*

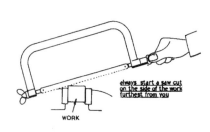

Fig. 2 *Starting the saw cut.*

RIGHT

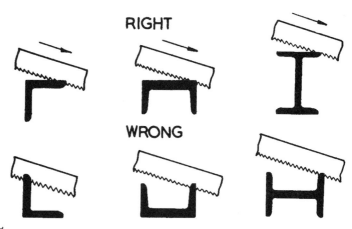

WRONG

Fig. 3 *Sawing angle and channel sections.*

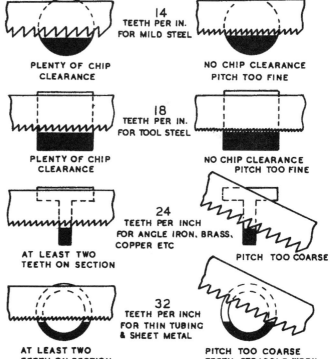

14 TEETH PER IN. FOR MILD STEEL

PLENTY OF CHIP CLEARANCE

NO CHIP CLEARANCE PITCH TOO FINE

18 TEETH PER IN. FOR TOOL STEEL

PLENTY OF CHIP CLEARANCE

NO CHIP CLEARANCE PITCH TOO FINE

24 TEETH PER INCH FOR ANGLE IRON, BRASS, COPPER ETC

AT LEAST TWO TEETH ON SECTION

PITCH TOO COARSE

32 TEETH PER INCH FOR THIN TUBING & SHEET METAL

AT LEAST TWO TEETH ON SECTION

PITCH TOO COARSE TEETH STRADDLE WORK

Fig. 4 *Choosing the correct tooth pitch.*

43

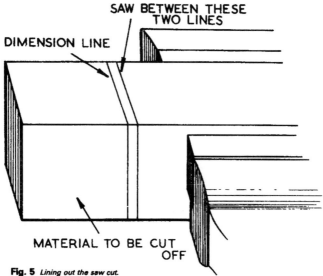

DIMENSION LINE

SAW BETWEEN THESE
TWO LINES

MATERIAL TO BE CUT
OFF

Fig. 5 *Lining out the saw cut.*

The selection of correct tooth pitch is, of course, of the utmost importance. It is therefore disappointing to find that, for the most part, local stockists carry only one pitch of saw blade (usually 24 teeth per inch or 24 teeth in 25m/m) for general use.

If we look at Fig. 4 it is clear that such a blade is not fitted for general purposes and that such a condition is not realisable. It would seem, therefore, that blades of 18 pitch are desirable and worth stocking.

Whenever practicable, large material to be cut off should be lined out in accordance with Fig. 5. In this way one can check the progress of the cut and its accuracy, and avoid waste of material by so doing.

The practice of 'bundling', that is the grouping together of similar sections of stock for sawing, is perhaps more applicable to work for the power hacksaw. Nevertheless, angle material, for example, can be bundled with advantage sometimes. To do so, of course, would require the work to be lined out as described in the previous paragraph, if success is to result. This matter will be dealt with comprehensively in Chapter 6, 'Using the Hacksawing Machine', later in Part 2.

PART 2
CHAPTER 4

Bench Mounted Hacksaw Machines

An intermediate stage between the hand hacksaw and the power machine was introduced many years ago by Goodell-Pratt of America. This consisted of a pair of uprights set in a metal base and supporting a framework on which a carriage could slide. A suitable hacksaw frame was fixed to this carriage enabling the user to saw accurately any material or work placed in the vice mounted on the baseplate.

Many years ago, requiring some means of accurately slitting a number of components, the author constructed the machine as in Fig. 1. The make-up of the device will be clear from the illustration. In view of the nature of the work for which it was intended, a pair of

Fig. 1 *The bench-mounted hand hacksaw.*

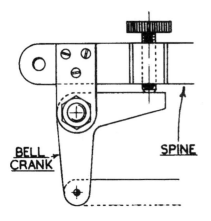

BELL CRANK

SPINE

Fig. 2 *Method of tensioning the saw blade, devised by the author.*

to adjust the position of the work in relation to the saw as well as making maximum use of the blade itself.

The actual saw frame may not be without interest. It was thought, as indeed it is, essential that the saw blade should remain truly vertical when tensioned. For this reason the somewhat novel method of applying tension depicted in Fig. 2 was devised.

The action of the tensioner should be evident from the illustration, where it will be appreciated that the function of the bell-crank is to pull the saw blade in a dead straight line when the tension wheel is turned.

Bench Mounted Power Hacksawing Machines

From time to time there has been a number of small power hacksaws put on the market. These, for the most part, were intended for bench mounting, where they were most conveniently located for the use of the mechanics

stops were fitted to the uprights. The mounting for the vice is also seen in the illustration. This consists of two parts, a base plate superimposed by an adjustable plate to which the vice itself is fixed. This arrangement allows the user

Fig. 3 *The Pacera bench hacksaw.*

Fig. 3A *Sketch of the Pacera hacksaw.*

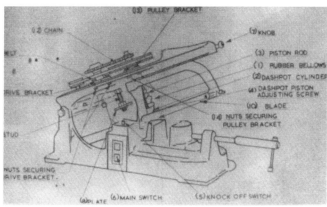

Labels visible:
(13) PULLEY BRACKET
(12) CHAIN
(7) KNOB
(3) PISTON ROD
(1) RUBBER BELLOWS
(2) DASHPOT CYLINDER
(4) DASHPOT PISTON ADJUSTING SCREW
(10) BLADE
(14) NUTS SECURING PULLEY BRACKET
DRIVE BRACKET
STUD
NUTS SECURING DRIVE BRACKET
(8) PLATE
(6) MAIN SWITCH
(5) KNOCK OFF SWITCH

Fig. 3B *Specification of the Pacera bench hacksaw.*

4" HACKSAWING MACHINE

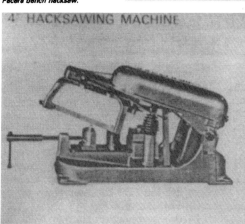

The 4" Hacksaw Machine is based on an entirely new design concept and features a unique horizontal drive mechanism. All working parts are readily accessible in the head of the machine and the very compact arrangement of primary and secondary drive with close shaft centres ensures smooth running whilst being highly efficient.

This machine is built on a heavy cast iron bed section. All moving parts, including the driving motor, are mounted in the 'head' of the machine thus concentrating useful weight at the most advantageous position, i.e. above the saw.

The machine is equipped with an oil dash pot to control the fall of the bow and this control is variable to ensure most efficient cutting of any material. The range of control provided can easily be adjusted to suit differing conditions but all machines are despatched from the Works with the control adjusted for average use. The machine is arranged to cut on the forward stroke, the dash pot providing the necessary relief of the blade on the return stroke.

4" HACKSAWING MACHINE		
Cutting Capacity at 90°	4"	102 mm.
Cutting Capacity at 45°	2"	51 mm.
Length of Stroke	4"	102 mm.
Blade Size	12"	305 mm.
Cutting Strokes per Minute	150	
Motor	½ h.p.	
Base Fixing Centres		
— Bench Model	27¼" x 8¼"	690 x 222 mm.
— Floor Model	31½" x 9¾"	800 x 248 mm.
Weight net — Bench Model	178 lbs.	81 kgs.
— Floor Model	210 lbs.	95 kgs.
Standard Equipment	— ½ h.p. Motor, Swivel Vice, Built-in no volt and overload release starter.	
Extra Equipment	— Floor Stand.	

47

Fig. 4 *Bench hacksaw by E.W. Cowell Ltd.*

and fitters for whom they were intended.

Some of these machines were fully finished and fitted with a driving motor, others were supplied as castings and other necessary material but with some of the difficult machining already completed.

Amongst the former the hacksaw in Fig. 3 made by W. J. Meddings is an example.

This is a particularly interesting machine, having some very novel features in its design. Figs. 3(a) and 3(b) will perhaps reveal the nature of some of them. The most enterprising feature is the setting of the crankshaft vertically with reduction arrangements and the final drive to the crankshaft set horizontally. Almost as interesting is the use of the driving motor as a counterpoise. The machine is fitted with an oil dashpot in order to regulate the rate of down feed for the saw blade, and an automatic knock-off is provided to stop the driving motor as soon as the sawing operation has been completed.

Another example, not illustrated, is the machine made by Kennedy. This had a capacity of 2 inches and was of simple but robust construction.

Of the part-machined examples the hacksaw offered by E. W. Cowell of Watford is probably the best known. This machine, designed by Bowyer-Lowe, is fitted with a relieving device to take the load off the saw teeth on the return stroke. See Fig. 4.

In this connection James Neill, the makers of hacksaw blades, have stated that in their opinion the use of a relieving device on machines where only hand blades are fitted is somewhat irrelevant. They are continually making tests on hand hacksaw blades fitted in special machines without relief, and are finding that no undue shortening of blade life results.

This finding is amply borne out by the author's experience with a home-made machine introduced some years ago. This machine was of very simple construction so had no relief device. It made use of standard 10" hand blades in the first instance, though in a later design the blade length was reduced to an effective 5" by cutting down the saw blade with an elastic grinding wheel.

The original test machine is depicted in Fig. 5 where its starkness will be apparent. However, it did yeoman service and is still in use 25 years after it was first put to work.

The final design as realised by 'Duplex' is in Fig. 6. It will be seen that several additions have been made to the original conception, notably that of the sliding weight enabling increased pressure to be put on the saw blade when needed.

It should perhaps be explained that the carriage, upon which the saw frame is mounted, runs on ball races travelling in the slot seen in the carriage arm B and that the saw cut can be adjusted within limits by raising or lowering the fulcrum standard A to allow the saw cut to finish parallel with the base of the vice. The stop K can be adjusted to limit the travel of the carriage arm once the position on the work for finishing the cut has been determined.

Fig. 5 *Test machine for the author's hacksaw.*

When setting work in the vice, provision has to be made that will allow the carriage arm to be held up during the process. This is effected by the Trigger F engaging the Stop E under the control of the Push Rod H. The Stop E is attached to the Guide Arm D, while the Push Rod has a return spring set in the rear Counterweight Support C.

Fig. 7 depicts the obverse of the machine set up as a lathe attachment.

Fig. 6 *Final design of the author's hacksaw machine.*

Fig. 7 *The author's machine as a lathe attachment.*

Fig. 8 *The hacksaw attachment mounted on the lathe.*

So far as the author is aware this is the only instance of the power hacksaw being made an attachment for the lathe. If there are others the author would be glad to hear about them.

As a lathe attachment the machine is mounted on a pair of parallel packing pieces B. These are aligned with the bed of the lathe by means of the guide A while the machine as a whole is secured by the bolt C.

The Hacksaw Attachment is depicted mounted on the lathe in Fig. 8.

Fig. 9 *An early example of a light commercial power hacksaw.*

50

CHAPTER 5

The Power Hacksaw

Floor Mounted Machines

For heavier duty than can be expected from bench-mounted saws it is necessary to provide independent supports that will enable the machines to be bolted to the floor, thus, perhaps, giving greater stability. Of equal importance, however, is the increased accessibility that is given by this independence; plenty of room round the hacksaw is a prerequisite if long pieces of material are to be handled with safety and speed.

At one time there was on the market a number of light floor-mounted machines with a maximum capacity round about 3", that adequately filled the needs of the small machine shop but were lacking in the versatility required in the larger establishments.

A typical example of a light machine is shown in Fig. 1(a). No relieving arrangements were provided but a counterweight was fitted; this could be adjusted either to lighten or increase the load on the saw blade according to the class of work being undertaken.

No comparable machine seems available today so it seems that the amateur, at all events, must build for himself a contrivance that best suits his capabilities, unless of course he wishes to purchase a professionally-made machine.

Commercial Hacksawing Machines

Historically, there have been many designs of hacksawing machine in the past, varying from the very light to something heavier as befits the work it may be called on to perform.

Fig. 1 *A light power hacksaw (very similar to that opposite).*

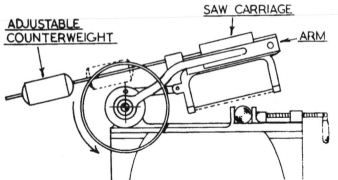

ADJUSTABLE COUNTERWEIGHT

SAW CARRIAGE

ARM

Fig. 1A *The simple power hacksaw.*

As an example of a light saw Fig. 1 is representative of equipment available, about the turn of the century, for a very few pounds. The illustration is taken from a somewhat historic catalogue published in 1910, and the price tag (£5.50) speaks for itself.

The make-up of the saw had all the essentials including a stop enabling repetitive length cutting to be carried

Fig. 2 *A modern 8 inch capacity hacksaw.*

out. A counterpoise was fitted so that pressure applied to the work through the saw blade could be varied.

The Power Hacksaw

Modern hacksaw machines have either prismatic or square section slides for the saw carriage. The simple machine illustrated had a pair of parallel bars upon which the frame for the saw carriage could slide much on the lines of the device in Fig. 1 of Chapter 4.

As with so many of these tools no countershaft was provided, nor was there any accommodation for independent motor drive since at the time these machines were made, none was available. Instead the drive was taken directly from the lineshafting, a hand-operated clutch on the saw's crankshaft being used to stop and start the machine. An example of such a saw in the author's possession gave splendid service for many years. It seems a pity that no comparable commercially produced saw is available today, for this is ideal equipment for the amateur and small professional workshop whose owners obviously will not be prepared to pay a high price for a tool whose use cannot possibly be described as anything else but intermittent.

At the other end of the scale the machine depicted in Fig. 2 is representative of modern practice. This saw, with a capacity of 8″, mounts a 16″ blade and has a working stroke of 6¼″. Two cutting speeds are available, 65 strokes per minute and 105 strokes per minute. A hydraulic variable feed is provided; this incorporates mechanism that gives relief to the saw blade on the return stroke.

The vice fitted to the machine has both jaws capable of movement axially. The arrangement allows the operator to make use of the whole saw blade once some part of it has become blunted: this is effected by moving the standing jaw along and securing it to bring the work under a fresh section of the saw.

Hydraulic Variable Feed and Blade Relieving Systems

For the most part commercially produced hacksaw machines are provided with variable down feed for the saw blade and this is sometimes supplemented by devices to give relief to the blade on the back stroke.

The variable down feed is commonly provided by an oil-filled dashpot having its piston attached to the saw carriage arm which is supported by the oil in the dashpot pressing against the underside of the piston itself. A typical dashpot may be seen attached to the 3″ capacity machine made by the author and described later in the chapter. The dashpot is a simple device consisting of a cylinder closed at one end and provided with a transfer port having a needle control valve at its upper end. When the saw carriage arm is raised it carries with it the piston to the top of its stroke. The piston is provided with a disc valve on its lower face. Consequently, as soon as the carriage arm is released the valve

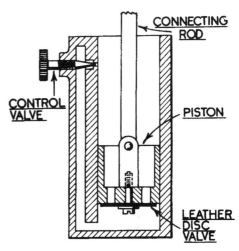

Fig. 3 *The Dashpot.*

closes and the oil supports the arm by means of the piston which is now held stationary. However, as soon as the control valve is opened oil passes up

Fig. 3A *A typical mounting for the dashpot.*

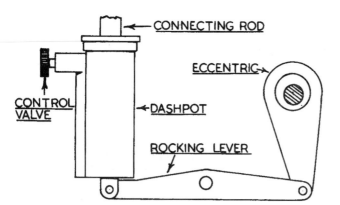

CONNECTING ROD

ECCENTRIC

CONTROL VALVE

DASHPOT

ROCKING LEVER

Fig. 4 Saw blade relief mechanism.

the transfer pipe into the top of the cylinder allowing the arm and the saw carriage to descend. The rate of descent, and consequently the feed of the saw itself, can then be adjusted by the

Fig. 4A Saw relief mechanism fitted to the "Duplex" hacksaw.

control valve, and set to any required value.

The arrangement is depicted diagrammatically in Fig. 3.

Fig. 3(a) depicts a typical installation of the dashpot. The device in question is one designed for E. W. Cowell's bench hacksaw machine and was made up by the author in order to test the possibilities of hydraulic down feed.

Relieving mechanism also comprises an oil dashpot. Whereas in the automatic feed the cylinder of the dashpot is fixed, in the relieving mechanism the cylinder floats, supported on a rocking lever actuated either by a cam or an eccentric attached to the hacksaw's crankshaft, as depicted in Fig. 4.

Fig. 4(a) shows a blade-relieving device fitted by the author to the 'Duplex' hacksaw. This device follows the lines of that depicted in Fig. 4. The eccentric gives the saw blade a clearance of approximately an eighth-of-an-inch, allowing the cut to be resumed as soon as the working stroke commences.

The action of the system is quite simple, and should be easily understood from the illustration. The interior arrangements of the dashpot are similar to that of the hydraulic feed already described. Consequently, when the casing of the dashpot is lifted by the rocking lever, the oil within closes the valve in the piston, which is then lifted by the continuing movement of the lever pushing up the connecting rod and so elevating the carriage arm of the saw itself.

All of this in no way impairs the action of the automatic feed which continues to function under the control of the bypass valve itself.

One should perhaps point out that the drive to the rocking lever needs to be timed accurately to ensure that the lift to the carriage arm is given on the right stroke.

The machine in Fig. 5 and Fig. 6 was made by the author, largely from scrap material, in order to supplement the 'Duplex' hacksaw described earlier and to make use of standard 10″ handsaw blades, so avoiding the cutting down of the normal handsaw blades as required for the 'Duplex' machine.

The bed is made from 1⅛″ hardwood faced with mild steel plate, a combination that has proved very successful.

The drive is through a 30-1 worm reduction gearbox, the shaft carrying the worm wheel acting as the crankshaft for the machine. The hacksaw is designed to make 60 strokes per minute and the drive from the motor to give effect to this is by means of a ¼″ round rubber-canvas endless belt running on 4″ diameter pulleys. These belts are the product of Greengate Industrial Polymers Limited of Salford, Lancashire, England who it is hoped may be so able to arrange sales matters that individual belts will be available to amateur and small workshop users.

The motor is set on a swinging mount that may be set positively to put the correct tension on the belt.

Figs. 5 and 6. *The Author's Hacksaw.*

Some work has been carried out on the machine in order to establish the possibility of providing some relief for the saw blade. Indeed the work still goes on, despite assurances from James Neill, who make saw blades, that provided the operating speed is kept low the wear on hand saw blades is little affected if no relief is provided.

Counterbalance weights have been fitted and the spindle upon which they move has an anchorage that permits it to be set either before or behind the fulcrum centre on which the arm carrying the saw frame swings. With the weight behind the fulcrum centre the counterbalance can be set so that $1/16''$ box section material (the legs on which the machine itself stands for example) can be cut without fear of evil consequences. Alternatively, when cutting large diameter material the weight needs to be set forward of the fulcrum centre.

Since the above was written the author has had some experience with the relieving device now fitted to the 'Duplex' hacksaw machine. There is little doubt that this device has proved satisfactory in every way and has had a marked effect on saw blade life.

It was decided, therefore, to apply the same mechanism to the larger hacksaw in the workshop. The equipment follows closely that shown in Fig. 4. That is to say the dashpot floats on a rocking lever extension to the saw's crankshaft.

The equipment in Fig. 6(a) shows that a bellows has been fitted to the dashpot in order to keep out swarf and dirt.

Subsequent work on the machine has led to the fitting of an oil dashpot to regulate the down-feed of the saw blade. In addition a micro-switch has been added in order to cut out the driving motor as soon as the saw has finished its work.

'Cardboard Engineering'
Under this heading a few words on the design of the machine may not be out

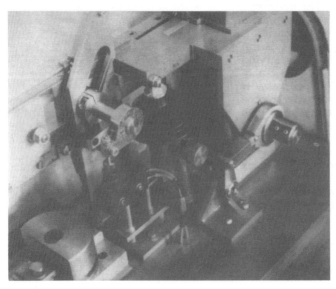

Fig. 6A *The Relieving Device.*

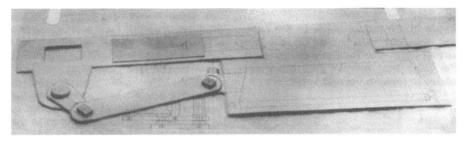

Fig. 7 *The "Cardboard Engineering" simulator.*

of place. A lot of drawing time can be saved if, instead of making a whole series of detailed drawings in order to find out what occurs to various components in their working cycle, a simple full scale representation of the parts to be investigated is made in cardboard. This can then be used to simulate the actual working of the mechanism.

The method described was employed when designing the hacksaw depicted in Fig. 5 and Fig. 6 and the actual simulation employed is shown in Fig. 7.

This enabled a number of small problems to be solved quickly and the component position to be established.

The Vice
For the simple type of power-operated saw the vice fitted, for the most part, can only accommodate work that will be cut at right angles to its axis. In the larger type of saw, however, in order to exploit its capacity to the full, the vice must be capable of angular setting.

The vice in Fig. 8 is typical. Both jaws are movable radially, so the work may be set at any angle that may be required.

Fig. 8 *The Vice.*

Selecting Tooth Size

Before fitting a new blade to the hacksaw machine one must choose the correct tooth size for the work in hand. The table that follows will assist the reader to make a correct selection.

Material	Recommended Teeth per inch		
Alloy Steels	6	10*	
Aluminium	6	10	
Brass	4	6	10
Bronze	6	10	
Carbon Tool Steel	6	10*	
Case Hardening Steel	6	10	
Cast Iron	4	6	10
Cold Rolled Steel	4	6	10
Copper	6	10	
Cupro Nickel	6	10	
Drill Steel	6	10	14*
Duralumin	6	10	
High Speed Steel	6	10*	
Gauge Steel	6	10*	
Heat Resisting Steel	6	10	14*
Machinery Steel	4	6	
Malleable Iron	4	6	10
Silver Steel	6	10*	
Stainless Steel	6	10	14
Tubing, Conduit	10	14	

The table above, reproduced by the kindness of James Neill and Co. makers of 'Eclipse' saw blades, refers to blades suitable for use in heavy hacksaws. For recommendations applying to light machines the table reproduced in Chapter 2 should be consulted as the information contained in it applies to light power machines as well as to the handsaws with which the chapter is concerned.

It should be noted that figures marked with an asterisk indicate that a high-speed steel blade is recommended.

Fitting the Saw Blade

The mounting of the saw blade so that it is truly upright is of vital importance to the satisfactory working of the power hacksaw. This is a matter that has already been stressed in connection with hand-held saws.

It is also of importance that the tension on the blade should be correct, otherwise the resulting cut is likely to be crooked and may cause breakage. The correct sequence for tensioning the saw blade is as follows:

I. Place the blade on the pins A in the blade holder

II. Turn the nuts B on the blade holder until they are finger tight

III. Apply the correct number of turns to the tension nut (in the absence of other instructions turn it finger tight plus one full turn)

IV. Tighten the nuts of the blade holder with a spanner

The parts referred to in the above instruction are detailed in Fig. 9.

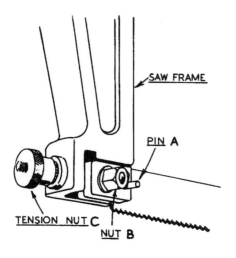

SAW FRAME

PIN A

TENSION NUT C

NUT B

Fig. 9 *Parts of the blade tensioning device.*

Sawing Failures and their Causes

The causes of the failures that can be encountered when using a power driven hacksaw may be grouped under four headings:

1. Blade breakages
a) Insufficient tension of the blade, or excessive tension if breakage occurs at the pin holes
b) Cutting a thin section on a sharp corner with too much pressure on the blade, or with a blade having too coarse a pitch
c) Using too light a blade with too heavy a feed
d) Material working loose in the vice
e) Using a new blade in a cut made by an old blade

2. Blade dulling quickly
a) Low tungsten steel blade being used where a high speed steel blade is essential, for example on hard material
b) Incorrect tooth pitching
c) Blade fitted with teeth pointing in the wrong direction
d) Excessive speed
e) Excessive pressure on the blade
f) Insufficient pressure. Saw teeth rub instead of biting into the work
g) Failure to use a proper coolant

3. Teeth of the saw blade ripping out
a) Tooth pitch too coarse when cutting thin sections
b) Sawing against a sharp corner with less than three consecutive teeth in contact with the work
c) Material moving during the sawing operation

4. The saw cuts crooked
a) Blade held insecurely or out-of-square
b) Blade insufficiently tensioned
c) Hard spot in material forcing the blade out of line. To overcome the trouble turn the work over and start from the other side. If necessary fit a new blade
d) Material working loose in vice
e) Saw frame out of line

It is of great importance to see that the machine is run at the correct speeds.

These are 70 strokes per minute for hard materials and 120 for soft stock. These figures apply to High Speed Steel blades using a coolant on all material except on cast iron or nickel chrome steels which should be sawn dry.

A suitable coolant comprises water in which soda and a small portion of soluble oil has been mixed.

CHAPTER 6

Using the Power Hacksaw

In previous chapters we have considered many salient points that govern the selection and application of the correct hacksaw blade for a particular class of work. We must now consider some of the common jobs that are performed on the hacksawing machine.

Mounting the Work

Clearly, any work set up for sawing must be held firmly or damage to the saw blade must result. For the most part the work will be caught in a machine vice capable of holding material of the maximum size for which the hacksaw has been designed. In addition the vice jaws can be set at an angle to

deal with any work needing this facility.

The vice may take several forms; it may either form part of the machine as seen in the Pacera Hacksaw or it may be a self-contained unit such as is fitted to the Cowell machine.

Perhaps one of the simplest, though not by any means the least useful holding device is that depicted in Fig. 1.

In this pattern a T-slotted base is affixed to the bed of the machine and is positioned so that there is a clearance of approximately half-an-inch between the saw frame members and the edge of the vice jaws. The jaws themselves are movable along the slotted base, thus enabling the operator to make full

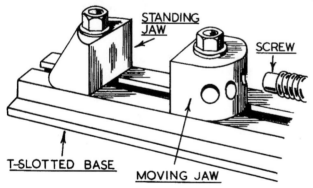

STANDING JAW

SCREW

T-SLOTTED BASE

MOVING JAW

Fig. 1 *Machine vice for the hacksaw.*

use of the whole saw blade itself, instead of confining the wear to a relatively small part of it.

Pressure is applied to the moving jaw either by means of a lever having a cam formed on its extremity, or a screw passing through the centre of a block, both having anchorages set on the slotted base. In the case of the screw, the block may engage slots machined across the face of the slotted base as seen in Fig. 2.

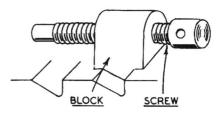

Fig. 2 *Application of the pressure screw.*

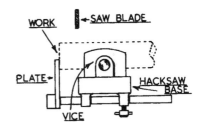

Fig. 3 *The length stop.*

Where long lengths of material have to be sawn some form of stand needs to be provided in order to support the bar during the operation. This applies particularly to repetition sawing when the length stop fitted to the hacksawing machine is in use.

The Length Stop
Most commercial hacksaws are provided with an adjustable stop enabling the user to set the saw to cut repetitively any length of material required. These stops are, for the most part, of simple conception and are, of course, easy to use. They consist of a rod, sliding in lugs forming part of the hacksaw base casting, and having a plate or outer abutment attached to it. The plate is set at a distance from the saw blade equal to the length of the pieces of material it is required to produce. The arrangement is set out in Fig. 3.

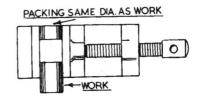

Fig. 4 *Sawing short lengths of material.*

Clearly, little difficulty need be experienced in holding those pieces of material or parts that engage the full width of the vice jaws. Small pieces, however, need special treatment if they are to be sawn successfully.

Fig. 4 depicts a method frequently used for the purpose by the author.

In order to ensure that the work remains level when being sawn it will pay to support it with a jack, as in Fig. 5.

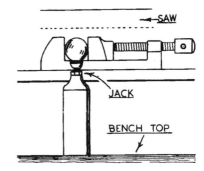

Fig. 5 *Supporting short lengths of material.*

61

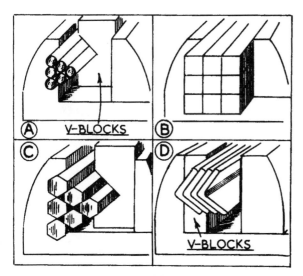

Fig. 6 *"Bundling"*.

This method is particularly useful when employed with bench-mounted machines. However, provided sufficient firm packing is available the method is equally applicable to a floor-mounted hacksaw. With the bench machine the author employs a standard machinist's jack, or a car jack if the floor-mounted hacksaw is in use, with again, sufficient rigid packing to ensure a firm support for the jack itself.

'Bundling'

As its name suggests this is the practice of grouping together a number of similar pieces of material and holding them in the vice so that a number of identical lengths can be treated for sawing at the one setting. For the most part it is short lengths of metal that lend themselves to bundling since long lengths would be too difficult to handle in this way. The practice may be applied to any material of regular section.

Thus 'bundling' may be used with round, square, hexagon or angle section metal that will 'nest' within the vice jaws with or without additional support.

Fig. 6 demonstrates the four examples of 'bundling' to which reference has been made. It will be noticed that in three instances V-blocks are used to support the work. In the case of the round material depicted at A it is probable that, for the most part, a pair of V-blocks will be needed as also will the example illustrated at C.

Square section metal, as seen in diagram B, is best held between pieces of card place between the vice jaws and the material itself. In this way any very slight inequalities there may be in the sizes of the individual pieces will be counterbalanced and the work held firmly.

In some machine vices a V-groove is machined horizontally across the face of its standing jaw. This would be a satisfactory alternative to the V-blocks indicated in example D.

PART 2
CHAPTER 7

The Fretsaw

The Fretsaw and Jigsaw
So far we have been considering saws, both hand and mechanically operated, that are intended for sawing in a straight line. It is clear, however, that the ability to execute curved work is essential to much workshop activity, an ability that extends back many years.

In the author's copy of Holtzapffel's 'Turning and Mechanical Manipulation' Vol II 1846 these matters, as usual, are dealt with at some length, particular attention being given to the use of the special saws used in buhl or marquetry work. These saws are similar to the present day fretsaws and piercing saws in Fig. 1 and Fig. 2.

The fretsaw has a deep-throated frame enabling it to be employed on relatively large areas of work. Tension on the saw blade is maintained by springing the frame while the saw blade is being mounted. The piercing saw seen in Fig. 2 has the same make-up as the fret-

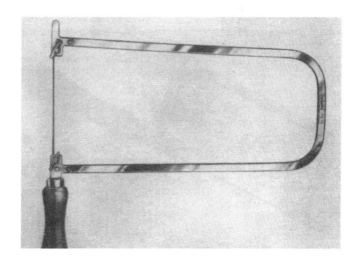

Fig. 1 *The hand fretsaw.*

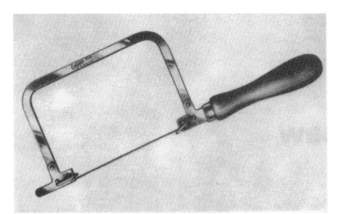

Fig. 2 *The piercing saw.*

saw; the blade is secured in the same way by means of a pair of clamps and is tensioned by springing the frame.

In the piercing saw in Fig. 3, however, tension is applied to the blade by more positive methods. As will be seen the spine of the frame is carried in a lug in the cast member forming the main element of the saw itself. A clamp screw in this member serves to secure the spine in the correct position to obtain maximum tension on the blade. Pressure is applied by gripping the cast member in the right hand and squeezing while the thumb is applied to the end of the frame. The left hand can then be used to turn the screw that secures the two elements together.

The Fretsaw Blade
Blades for use in the fretsaw, whether by hand or in the machine, are divided

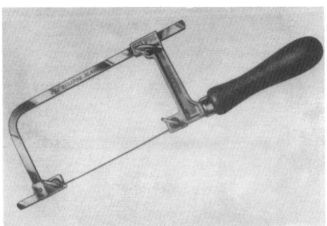

Fig. 3 *The modern piercing saw.*

64

TABLE 1 PIERCING SAW BLADES

Blade	Thickness and Width of Blade	Pitch of Tooth	Thickness of Material	Type of Work
M 4/0	.006" x .018"	80	Up to .015"	For extremely fine and delicate scroll work
M 3/0	.007" x .019"			A slightly stronger blade for less intricate scroll work
M 2/0	.008" x .021"	60	.016" to .030"	For intricate scroll work
M 1/0	.009" x .023"			A slightly stronger blade for less intricate scroll work
M 0	.010" x .025"			A stronger blade for general use
M 1	.011" x .026"	52	.031" to .045"	For either scroll or straight work
M 2	.012" x .027"	44	.046" to .060"	For scroll work
M 3	.014" x .030"			A stronger blade for general use
M 4	.015" x .032"	32	.061" to .092"	For scroll work
M 5	.017" x .036"		.061" & over	A stronger blade for general use

Fig. 4 *Fretsaw blades for metal and wood.*

TABLE 2 FRETSAW BLADES

Blade	Thickness and Width of Blade	Pitch of Tooth	Thickness of Material	Type of Work
W 1/0	.011" x .034"	32	Up to 1/16"	For all intricate scroll work and general use on such very thin material
W 0	.011" x .037"	22	1/16" to 1/8"	For intricate scroll work
W 1	.014" x .039"			A stronger blade for less intricate work
W 2	.014" x .043"	18	1/8" to 1/4"	For scroll work
W 3	.014" x .047"			A stronger blade for general use
W 4	.017" x .051"	16	1/4" and above	For general use, each size being progressively stronger to suit individual requirements.
W 5	.020" x .055"			
W 6	.022" x .060"			

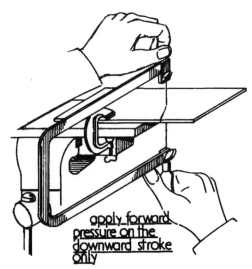

Fig. 5 *The author's simple fretsawing equipment.*

apply forward
pressure on the
downward stroke
only

by their manufacturers into three categories. In addition blades are available for employment in the jig saw.

The categories are: Piercing Saw, Fret Saw, Spiral Saw and Jig Saw Blades. Their salient dimensions are given in the accompanying tables. While the applications of the majority of the categories will be evident, the use of spiral saw blades may be unfamiliar. These blades are used for cutting materials that are likely to clog the teeth of fretsaw or piercing saw blades. They are particularly satisfactory when used on plastics or acrylic resins. As they will cut in any direction without the saw frame itself being turned they make the work of contour-sawing in difficult materials that much easier.

Piercing saw blades have been made according to the sizes given in the accompanying Table 1. It may be, however, that by the time these notes are printed some sizes will have been discontinued as the result of rationalisation. It may be, however, that stocks of some of the discontinued sizes may still be available at dealers. The same remarks also apply to the other tables which follow.

Fretsaws

As will be appreciated fretsaw blades are for the most part intended for use on wood. Consequently the tooth pitching tends to be much coarser than that employed with piercing saw blades.

In Table 2 the available saw blades are listed together with the thickness of work for which the individual blades are suited.

Fig. 4 demonstrates, on an enlarged scale, the difference between fretsaw blades intended for use on wood and those made to saw metal. The blade depicted at A is for use on wood and as will be seen, has a very coarse tooth pitching in order to provide adequate clearance of the chips formed during the sawing operation. These blades are sometimes called 'Skip tooth' blades.

The blade illustrated at B, on the other hand, is of the type employed when sawing metal, where chip clear-

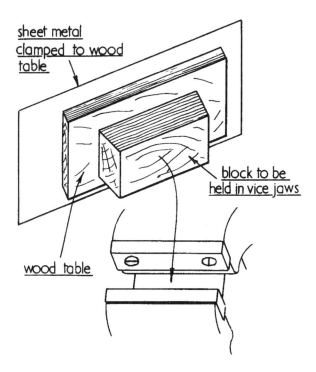

Fig. 6 *Method of using the bench vice for fretsawing.*

sheet metal clamped to wood table

block to be held in vice jaws

wood table

ance is not so important but where the tooth pitching needs to be tailored to the thickness of the metal from which the work is composed.

Using the Fretsaw and Piercing Saw
In the small workshop work needing to be sawn by the fretsaw or piercing saw occurs only sporadically. Accordingly, the work will usually have to be mounted as simply as possible using equipment already to hand. For the most part this means using the bench vice with the work supported on a small table gripped in the vice jaws.

The equipment used by the author is shown in Fig. 5 where the simple table held in the vice may be seen. The accompanying Fig. 6 shows the table

gripped in the vice with work held to it by a G-clamp so that it may be sawn in the manner prescribed.

Spiral Saws
It will be apparent that both piercing saws and fretsaws can only cut in one direction. For this reason, and in order to cope with modern plastics which tend to clog their teeth, spiral saw blades have been produced which obviate this trouble. In these blades the toothed portion is accurately spiralled. As a result the teeth do not clog or bind during the sawing process and, in addition the blades will cut in any direction without the saw frame itself being turned. It should perhaps be noted that the ends of the blade are left flat

TABLE 3 SPIRAL SAW BLADES

Pattern No.	Length	Material Width	Material Thickness	Pitch
S.1	5″	.024″	.011″	60 T.P.I.
S.2	5″	.028″	.014″	52 T.P.I.
S.3	5″	.032″	.017″	44 T.P.I.

TABLE 4 JIGSAW BLADES

Pattern Pinned	Unpinned	Width	Thickness	Teeth 25mm	Recommended cutting uses
A7P	A7	.250″	.028″	7	Wood, asbestos, wall board, plastics* etc., over 10mm thick
C7P	C7	.187″	.022″		
B10P	B10	.187″	.028″	10	Wood, asbestos, wall board, plastics* etc., from 4.5mm to 9mm thick
D10P	D10	.110″	.020″		
C16P	C16	.187″	.022″	16	Wood, metal and plastics* etc., from 3mm to 4.5mm thick
D16P	D16	.110″	.020″		
—	E16	.070″	.017″		
C22P	C22	.187″	.022″	22	Wood, metal and plastics* etc., from 2.5mm to 3mm thick
D22P	D22	.110″	.020″		
—	E22	.070″	.017″		
—	F22	.035″	.011″		
C32P	C32	.187″	.022″	32	Wood, metal and plastics* etc., from 1mm to 2mm thick
D32P	D32	.110″	.020″		
—	E32	.070″	.017″		
—	F32	.035″	.011″		

allowing them to be gripped firmly in the saw frame. Sizes that have been available are given in Table 3.

Jig Saw Blades

The blades provided for the jig saw are listed in Table 4. In addition to dimensional details, silhouettes showing the tooth pitching are also given. A word of explanation is perhaps needed in connection with the words 'pinned' and 'unpinned'. Some jigsaws have a positive grip for the saw blade. This is provided by pins passing through each end of the blade and engaging adapters in the mechanism of the jigsaw itself. The unpinned blades rely on friction only, in the same way as the blades in hand-operated saw-frames.

Choice of Blades for the Jig Saw

To obtain the best results a blade should be selected having a tooth pitch that will not straddle the material to be sawn. Put more simply, thin sections need a fine-tooth saw while coarser teeth are required when cutting wood or plastic materials.

Once the tooth pitch has been decided the thinnest blade available should be selected as this will ensure rapid sawing, that the cut is narrow and that the saw will turn easily.

Lubricants for Use with the Jig Saw

Jig saw blades work more easily if a lubricant is applied to the work.
Suitable lubricants are:

For Wood	Beeswax
For Metal	Light Oil
For Plastics	No lubricant

In the case of plastics, these tend to become overheated during the cutting process, so the blade tends to jam in the saw kerf. The only satisfactory solution to the problem is to direct a stream of cold air on to the blade as near as possible to the point of cut. This will cool the blade and prevent overheating the work.

In order to get the best results from fretsaw and piercing saw blades attention should be paid to the following points:

1. The blade must be fitted correctly and securely in the saw frame with the teeth pointing towards its handle. But first make sure that the faces of the clamp are clean and undamaged.

2. The saw must be used with the blade upright and with pressure applied on the down stroke only.

3. The saw should not be overworked or have too much pressure applied to it. It should be allowed to do the work itself.

4. Piercing saw blades should be lubricated with light oil before use.

CHAPTER 8

Power Fretsaws and Jigsaws

The Fretsaw Machine

In the interests of rapid and comfortable working it was inevitable that the hand-held fretsaws or jigsaws should be developed into power-operated machines. Some of these devices were of very light construction while others were large and were permanent fixtures in the building where they were housed.

An example of such a fretsaw is Fig. 1. The work table and driving mechanism including one blade holder are located on and inside a cast-iron floor pedestal whilst the corresponding blade holder and its supporting slide are suspended from the roof on a pendant provided with a laminated spring to keep the saw blade in tension. The spring, com-

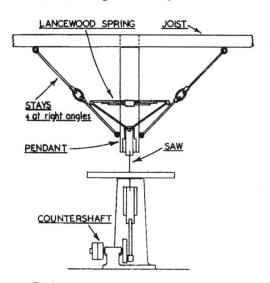

Fig. 1 *A large old-time power fretsaw.*

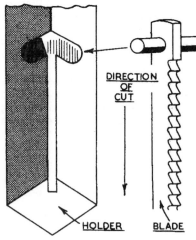

Fig. 2 *Method of attaching the saw blade.*

monly made from lancewood in these machines, is connected to the upper slide by means of a leather strap.

An interesting feature of this type of machine fretsaw is the method of mounting the saw blades which for the most part have cross-pins fitted at each end. The blade holders, or saw plungers as some term them, have hooks formed in them enabling them to be instantly attached or detached when required.

Fig. 2 depicts the method employed.

It is perhaps worth recalling that, as with hand-held fretsaws, the blade cuts on the down stroke as indicated in the illustration.

The lancewood mentioned earlier is chiefly imported from Guinea and, according to the 'Practical Woodworker', is light, hard, elastic and fine grained. It is commonly used, in some quarters, for bows and arrows as well as for fishing rods.

Fig. 2(a) depicts a model, now in the Science Museum, London, of an early

Fig. 2B *Hobbies fretsaw modern version.*

Fig. 2C *Hobbies fretsaw modern version, for bench use.*
Right, Fig. 2D *The original "Hobbies" fretsaw.*
Below, Fig. 2E *The American "Driver" fretsaw.*

OK Fretsaw Machine.

Frame and arms of steel. Tilting table. Arms give a swing of 19 in. and are made of light steel section. A spring fitted to the top arm adds greatly to free running and it raises the arm when the saw breaks. Sent ready for use with 12 saw blades, 2 designs, a drill bit, screwdriver and spanner. **37/6** Carriage forward.

power driven machine for piercing work on metal sheets or plates. Some of the work may be seen in the illustration.

The machine itself consists of a heavy cast-iron table supported on four legs and carrying a hollow V-shaped casting in which are set a pair of levers that terminate in the holders for the saw blade. The levers are connected together at one end by a rod and in the other by the saw itself which may be put under tension by a screw device fitted to the upper saw holder. This assembly is driven from a countershaft at the back of the machine by means of the connecting rod seen in the illustration.

The countershaft is fitted with a clutch that may be operated by a treadle at the front of the machine.

Of the very light machines many readers will remember the little machine made by Hobbies of Dereham, Norfolk, shown in Fig. 2(d). This was designed for the amateur at a time when fretwork was distinctly popular and the products of the pastime tended to litter many households.

American manufacturers have, at one time or another, put on the market fretsaw machines intended for both amateur and professional use. A good example from the Driver range of tools is depicted in Fig. 2(e). This machine had considerable throat, allowing quite large work to be handled with some facility. It dates from about 1938.

Industry has always found a use for the fretsaw or jigsaw, so much development work has been put into the machine.

The machine in Fig. 3 is intended for cutting wood, plastics, laminated material and Perspex. It can also be used as a filing machine. It is obtainable both as a bench or floor-mounted machine and has fine range of speeds, in fact four in all, namely 550, 800, 1090 and 1400 strokes a minute.

The work table, which is capable of tilting to 45 degrees, has a working surface 18″ by 18″ (457 x 457m/m).

A sectional drawing of the Meddings jigsaw is reproduced in Fig. 4. As will be noticed, the drive to the blade holder is by means of a device known as a Scotch Crank. In this mechanism no connecting rod is needed as the crank pin engages directly a phosphor bronze slider set in the housing prepared for it in the reciprocating rod attached to the blade holder.

The whole of the reciprocating mechanism is oil-immersed, oil seals being provided to prevent any leakage of lubricant. The slider (77) and the reciprocating rod (84) can be seen in Fig. 5 which demonstrates, in an exploded view, the various details that comprise the lower reciprocating assembly.

The upper assembly, again in exploded view, may be seen in Fig. 6. The actuating rod (17), square in section, is driven from the lower reciprocating

Fig. 3 *The Meddings fretsaw.*

73

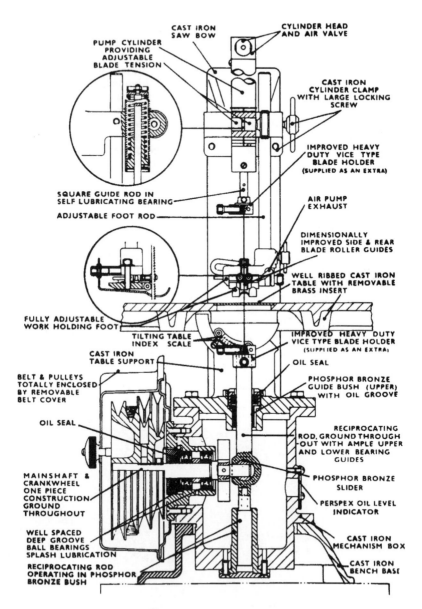

CYLINDER HEAD AND AIR VALVE

CAST IRON SAW BOW

PUMP CYLINDER PROVIDING ADJUSTABLE BLADE TENSION

CAST IRON CYLINDER CLAMP WITH LARGE LOCKING SCREW

IMPROVED HEAVY DUTY VICE TYPE BLADE HOLDER (SUPPLIED AS AN EXTRA)

SQUARE GUIDE ROD IN SELF LUBRICATING BEARING

ADJUSTABLE FOOT ROD

AIR PUMP EXHAUST

DIMENSIONALLY IMPROVED SIDE & REAR BLADE ROLLER GUIDES

WELL RIBBED CAST IRON TABLE WITH REMOVABLE BRASS INSERT

FULLY ADJUSTABLE WORK HOLDING FOOT

IMPROVED HEAVY DUTY VICE TYPE BLADE HOLDER (SUPPLIED AS AN EXTRA)

TILTING TABLE INDEX SCALE

CAST IRON TABLE SUPPORT

OIL SEAL

BELT & PULLEYS TOTALLY ENCLOSED BY REMOVABLE BELT COVER

PHOSPHOR BRONZE GUIDE BUSH (UPPER) WITH OIL GROOVE

OIL SEAL

RECIPROCATING ROD, GROUND THROUGH OUT WITH AMPLE UPPER AND LOWER BEARING GUIDES

MAINSHAFT & CRANKWHEEL ONE PIECE CONSTRUCTION GROUND THROUGHOUT

PHOSPHOR BRONZE SLIDER

PERSPEX OIL LEVEL INDICATOR

WELL SPACED DEEP GROOVE BALL BEARINGS SPLASH LUBRICATION

CAST IRON MECHANISM BOX

CAST IRON BENCH BASE

RECIPROCATING ROD OPERATING IN PHOSPHOR BRONZE BUSH

Fig. 4 *Section of the Meddings fretsaw.*

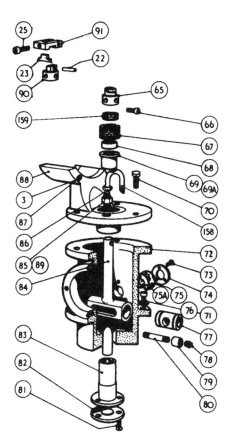

Fig. 5 *The reciprocating mechanism.*

exhaust deflector pump (158) to be seen in the previous illustration.

Fig. 7 demonstrates the general assembly of the main components of the jigsaw and, in this connection, the bow (157) is now a one-piece casting in the interests of rigidity and is not composed of two individual parts as may appear from the earlier Fig. 3.

The 'Duplex' Jigsaw
Some years ago the contributors 'Duplex', writing in *Model Engineer*, published the detail drawings of the jigsaw in Fig. 8. This is a small capacity machine with a work table suitable for cutting either wood or metal. The spring box, set above the table, not only contains the plunger supporting the upper

assembly via the saw blade that is caught in holders (18) and (65) attached to the rods themselves. The cylinder (12) is held in the bow (157) and houses a compression spring (16) to keep the saw blade in tension at all times.

The actuating rod (17) is fitted with a leather cup washer assembly converting the whole into a species of bicycle pump. Air from this device is delivered through the rubber hose (40) to the

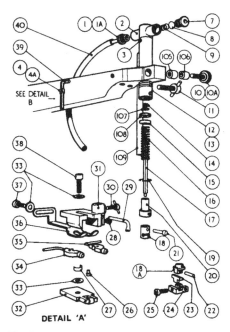

Fig. 6 *The upper assembly of the Meddings saw.*

75

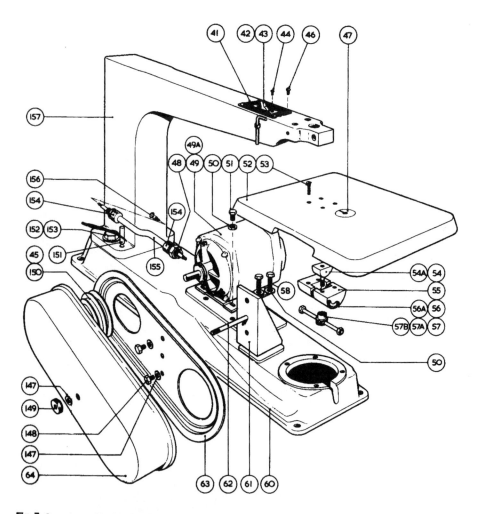

Fig. 7 *General assembly of the Meddings saw.*

end of the saw blade but also acts as the cylinder of the air pump used to blow away any wood dust or swarf produced when sawing. In this matter the machine follows accepted practice.

The drive to the saw blade is a little unusual, however. As may be seen in the illustration, the crankshaft is set under and behind the work table and has a disc crank supporting a short connecting rod attached to one end of the rocking lever. The opposite end of the lever is attached to a sliding member that acts as the lower support for the

saw blade to which it imparts the reciprocating motion it needs.

Fig. 9 depicts the mechanism used for taking the thrust from the saw blade when in work. As may be inferred, the two upper rollers restrain the blade from twisting while the lower roller supports the blade when work is pushed against it. Experience in using the jigsaw leaves the impression that a reversal of the location of these rollers might well be beneficial. It has always appeared to the author that the rollers resisting the twisting action are too far from the surface of the work which makes it

Fig. 9 (above) *Mechanism for absorbing the saw thrust on the Duplex jigsaw.*

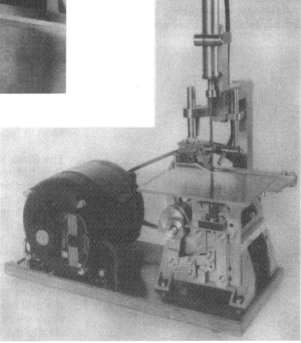

Fig. 8 *The "Duplex" jigsaw.*

77

Fig. 10 *Fences for the Duplex jigsaw.*

Below left, Fig. 11 *The Black and Decker jigsaw attachment.*

difficult to guide the work accurately when sawing.

As might be expected all the rollers are adjustable as, of course, is the foot

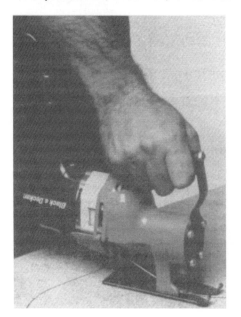

fitted to prevent the work from lifting off the work table.

In the same illustration may be seen the nozzle and part of the air pipe for the dust blower mentioned earlier. The height and placing of this nozzle is also adjustable.

Duplex, in addittition to designing the machine as a whole, provided drawings for some simple fences to be used with the jigsaw. A number of these may be seen in Fig. 10.

The Black and Decker Jig Saw
One further form of jig saw needs to be mentioned. This is the hand-held machine that may be used directly on the work as shown in Fig. 11. The tool depicted is the Black and Decker device marketed as an attachment to their electric power-drills. The tool is readily attached to the drill which remains nicely balanced when used in this way. Air from the cooling arrangements of the drill itself is ducted directly onto the work and so enables the worker to see clearly the line he has to follow.

CHAPTER 9

The Cold Saw

One cannot leave the subject of metal sawing without some reference to the cold saw and its use. The cold saw is a circular saw running at a slow speed, for the most part from 33r.p.m. to 65r.p.m., employed for the bulk in cutting to length of stock in the form of solid sections, tubes, pipes, extrusions etc. in the various materials that are available.

The cold saw was introduced during the last century in order to deal with the large sections of materials then coming to the fore in the wake of the Industrial Revolution then under way. Fig. 1 shows a form of saw appearing in suppliers' catalogues about the turn of the century. As will be seen the machine appears in two guises, one as a hand driven unit, the other as a saw that may be driven from the line shafting. The circular saw fitted was approximately 12" diameter and the maximum cutting capacity

Fig. 1 *Cold iron sawing machine.*

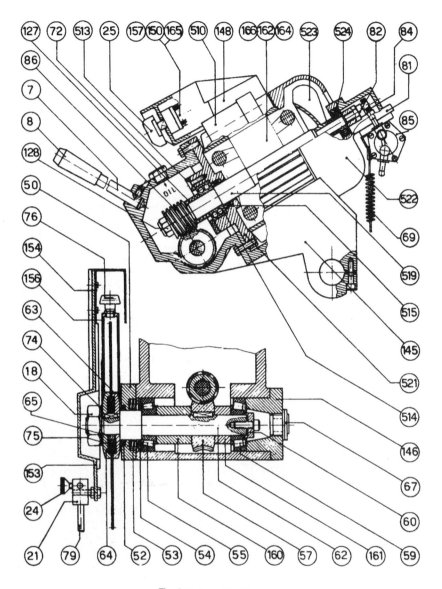

Fig. 3 *Section of the light cold saw.*

80

Fig. 2 *Modern light cold saw.*

8″ x 3″. A suds pump was fitted, the bed of the machine itself forming a trough to contain the lubricant.

An interesting design feature of this particular cold saw is the method used to drive the arbor on which the saw itself is mounted. The arbor carried a worm wheel which was engaged by a steel worm mounted on the shaft that was driven either by hand or from the shop lineshafting, the overall speed reduction being such that the saw would turn at a maximum of 60r.p.m., presumably.

The machine in Fig. 2 is a modern version of a light cold saw. Here, the worm drive has been retained enabling a compact motor-driven unit to be produced. A quick-acting vice is fitted in order to allow the rapid production of raw material billets when required. The vice has length stops so that repetition cutting can be undertaken.

The mechanism of the saw is shown in the sectional drawing Fig. 3 which is taken from the manufacturer's operating instructions sent out with each machine. This drawing depicts clearly the driving mechanism that is incorporated in the unit together with the disposition and type of the bearings used.

The machine is equipped with coolant equipment, a necessary provision for the work intended.

The quick-acting vice previously mentioned can be swung at any angle required to suit the work in hand, so an angular scale is provided in order to allow the vice to be set rapidly by the operator.

PART 2
CHAPTER 10

The Bandsaw

This is a machine in which an endless length of steel saw is carried on large diameter pulleys set one above the work table and one below, while the blade itself is threaded through guides able to protect it from any twisting movement that may be imparted by the work in hand.

Amongst other things, the bandsaw is intended for handling curved work. Consequently blades of varying width need to be fitted to accommodate the scale of the work being sawn. In addition straight dimensional sawing is within the capacity of the bandsaw, so for the most part the better class of machine is provided with fences, either built-in or as attachments, that will enable accurate cutting to a repetitive dimension to be carried out.

The bandsaw is a comparatively modern conception, being probably at the time of writing somewhat less than 100 years old. Many of the older machines must have been pretty lethal for there was little or no guarding for the saw, as two illustrations in my book 'A History of Machine Tools' make very clear.

Nowadays, government regulations have insisted that these machines are adequately guarded should a breakage of the saw occur. The operator would then be protected against the effects of any breakages.

Fig. 1 depicts a modern bandsaw in which the saw itself is almost entirely

Fig. 1A *Using the bandsaw.*

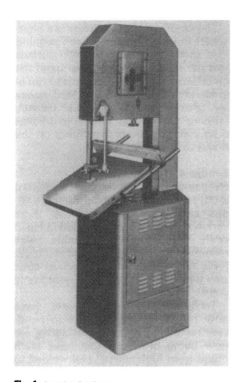

Fig. 1 *A modern bandsaw.*

brake to bring the saw to a stop rapidly when required.

The upper wheel is so mounted that the saw can be quickly adjusted for correct tension, a scale to give the operator the right setting for any given saw width being provided on the main frame. As to the wheel itself, this is mounted on sealed-for-life bearings that need no external lubrication and are, of course, proof against the ingress of any wood dust or other abrasive material.

The work table of the bandsaw is capable of tilting when needed. Fig. 2(a) demonstrates the method by which this is effected. As may be seen the table swivels on a mount that can be set at

Fig. 2 *A modern bandsaw with its protective doors open.*

covered in; in fact only the amount of exposure that is needed for any particular job should be given, and this is provided for by the pillar that carries the upper guide rollers. This is telescopic and can be adjusted vertically and locked at the desired position.

In Fig. 2 we see the machine with its cover doors open. This illustration also demonstrates very convincingly how well the operator is protected should there be a saw breakage.

On a constructional note, the main frame is a welded steel fabrication that carries the whole mechanism. The driving wheel is mounted directly on the motor which has a foot-operated

83

any desired angle up to 45°. It may also be observed that a stop is fitted, bolted to the main framework, that enables the operator to re-set the table truly at right angles to the saw itself once the angular cutting operation is completed.

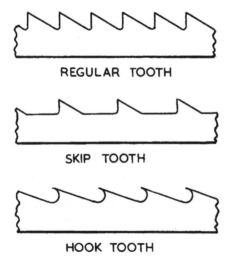

REGULAR TOOTH

SKIP TOOTH

HOOK TOOTH

Fig. 3 *Three variations of saw tooth.*

The woodworking bandsaw is a high-speed machine, the saw itself running at a speed from 2000 to 3000 surface feet per minute. On the other hand the metal working bandsaw needs to run at much lower speeds and, indeed, needs far greater latitude in this respect, ranging from 290ft. minimum to less than 75ft. minimum depending on the metal being sawn.

Bandsaw Blades

Bandsaws are made with three different tooth formations to accommodate various classes of material. The three variations of tooth are depicted in Fig. 3 while the accompanying table gives recommendations as to speed and tooth form when using a high-carbon steel saw which is the type most commonly used.

Technological developments have now brought improvements in bandsaw material. For example blades are now being produced that have teeth made from high-speed steel welded to a back formed from carbon alloy steel.

The composite saw blade enables the user to cut at an increased rate, while the increased resistance to flexing stresses conferred by the alloy steel backing greatly prolongs the useful life of the saw.

Table 2 gives the dimensions of bandsaws available whilst Table 1, already referred to, indicates the suitable tooth pitch for four specific thicknesses of work together with the correct speeds in feet per minute to be used with a wide variety of materials.

Tooth Set

The correct set of the teeth in a bandsaw is of importance to the user for a number of reasons. These are, perhaps in order of importance:

TABLE 1

Speed and Tooth Selection Table
High Carbon Bandsaw

	Speed ft./minute	Number of teeth per inch			
		Material thickness up to			
		¼"	½"	2"	4"
Low Carbon Steels	150–175	32/24R	18/14R	10/8R	6R
Medium Carbon Steels	100–150	32/24R	18/14R	10R	8R
High Carbon Steels	80–125	32/24R	18/14R	10R	10/8R
Low Carbon Free Cutting	150–175	24/18R	14/10R	8R	6R
Medium Carbon Free Cutting	100–150	24/18R	14/10R	8R	6R
Cast Iron	75–100	18R	14R	10R	8R
Nickel, Nickel Chrome, Nickel Chrome Molybdenum Steels	50–100	32/18R	14R	10R	8R
Tool and Die Steels	70–125	18R	14R	10R	8R
High Speed Steels	50–80	32/24R	18R	10R	10R
Stainless Steels	50–90	32/24R	18R	10R	8R
Heat Resisting Alloys, e.g., Nimonic, Titanium	30–45	32/24R	18/14R	10R	8R
Copper	250–1000	24/18R	14R/6H	6H	3H
Brass	250–1000	24/18R	14R/6H	6H	3H
Aluminium, Manganese, Phosphorus, Silicon, Bronzes	200–900	24/18R	14R/6H	6H	3H
Aluminium and Aluminium Alloys	500–1000	24/18R	14R/6S	4S	3S
Asbestos	400–800	18R	10R	6H	3H
Fibre Glass	500–1000	18R	10R	6H	3H
Formica	400–600	18R	14R	6H	3H
Plastics	1500–2500	14R	10R	6H	3H
Plywood	2000–3000	14R	6H	6H	3H

Recommended type of tooth
R—Regular   S—Skip   H—Hook

---

1. The correct set ensures an easy passage for the bandsaw through the work

2. It ensures a more accurate cut, particularly when cutting in a straight line

3. The right set provides a finer finish to the work

4. More even wear on the teeth results

Two types of tooth set are available; these are shown in Fig. 3(a). The Decker set, depicted to the left of the illustration, comprises a pattern of three teeth, one group set to the left, another group set over to the right with a third group of teeth remaining straight. This arrangement provides the optimum chip clearance. Decker set is recommended for extended runs on

TABLE 2

Carbon Steel Bandsaw

m/m	Regular Teeth inch	Teeth per 25m/m or 1"						
3 x 0.65	⅛ x 0.025				14	18	24	
3 x 0.65	3/16 x 0.025				14	18	24	32
5 x 0.65	¼ x 0.025			10	14	18	24	32
6 x 0.65	5/16 x 0.025			10	14	18	24	
8 x 0.65	3/8 x 0.025		8	10	14	18	24	
10 x 0.65	½ x 0.025		8	10	14	18	24	
16 x 0.80	5/8 x 0.032		8	10	14	18	24	
19 x 0.80	¾ x 0.032	6	8	10	14			
25 x 0.90	1 x 0.035	6	8	10	14			

m/m	Skip Teeth inch	Teeth per 25m/m or 1"		
6 x 0.65	¼ x 0.025			6
10 x 0.65	3/8 x 0.025	3		6
13 x 0.65	½ x 0.025	3		6
16 x 0.80	5/8 x 0.032	3		6
19 x 0.80	¾ x 0.032	3		
25 x 0.90	1 x 0.035	3	4	

m/m	Hook Teeth inch	Teeth per 25m/m or 1"	
13 x 0.65	½ x 0.025	3	6
19 x 0.80	¾ x 0.032	3	6
25 x 0.90	1 x 0.035	3	6

relatively heavy sections, say over ¼" thick. The set is also recommended for contour or profile cutting.

The Wavy set is a type in which groups of teeth are arranged alternately to the right and left of the blade. It is only supplied to selected sizes of regular tooth bandsaws. The set reduces to a minimum the danger of teeth ripping out, and for this reason is recommended for use on thin section material, that is under ¼" thick.

Bandsaw Breakages

There are several reasons for bandsaw breakage. One may take it that the material from which the saw is made is sure to be above reproach, for manufacturers check very strictly both the steel itself as well as the sharpening and, of course, the jointing of the saw.

If troubles do develop it is advisable for the user to contact the actual maker of his bandsaw. Meanwhile here are some possible reasons for breakage.

1. Crystallization of the steel ribbon from which the saw is made. This is a condition produced by the back of the saw rubbing against the metal disc of the saw guide. The disc should only revolve when the saw is actually cutting, otherwise it should be stationary.

2. Using a blade too wide for the radius of the curve being cut. The blade will therefore twist against the saw guides and may overheat so destroying the temper of the steel.

3. The use of worn or badly adjusted saw guides. These should support the blade as close to the point of sawing as possible.

4. Tension of the saw blade too great.

5. Forcing the feed. If the saw does not cut freely it may need resharpening.

6. Incorrect saw setting leading to the blade binding and overheating.

7. Incorrect sharpening of bandsaws for wood. Fig. 4 depicts the right and wrong methods. As shown the gullets at the base of the saw teeth should be rounded and not sharp, otherwise cracks will develop.

8. Finally, bad brazing of the joint. Check that the maker's instructions in this matter have been followed meticulously.

Perhaps it should be added that machine vibration is sometimes an unexpected source of saw breakage. When the pulley wheels have become worn or clogged with resin and wood fibres, or the machine itself is set on an unsecure foundation, then breakage may occur.

DECKER SET   WAVY SET

Fig. 3A *Bandsaw tooth setting.*

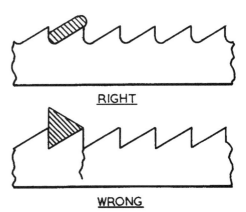

RIGHT

WRONG

Fig. 4 *Correct and incorrect method of sharpening bandsaws.*

CHAPTER 11

Bandsaw Brazers and Welders

The importance of correct bandsaw jointing has been mentioned in the previous chapter. Naturally, satisfactory procedure in this matter relies on the use of specialised equipment designed to ensure this.

Brazing the bandsaw joint is carried out by heating the work electrically, the electrical resistance of the joint causing it to rise to brazing heat. The equipment used comprises clamps to hold the saw in place and a lever and pressure pads to force the two halves of the joint into close contact as soon as the brazing material or silver solder has melted.

In order to preserve uniform blade thickness at the joint the work needs to be bevelled, the length of the bevel varying from ⅜" to ⅝" according to the width of the saw. In saws used for cutting wood the bevel or scarf should extend for two tooth pitches in accordance with Fig. 1.

Brazing Equipment
The equipment for brazing is sometimes attached to the column of the bandsaw itself, more particularly on saws intended for metal cutting in small general-purpose workshops where the operator himself usually carries out the brazing.

In the larger shop, however, the work is often the responsibility of a department, perhaps the millwrights, or the saw doctors in a wood mill, where the brazing equipment is bench-mounted.

Fig. 2 depicts a typical bandsaw brazer. This equipment is provided with a fence AA to ensure that the two ends of the bandsaw remain in alignment during the jointing process, a pair of clamps B to hold the work and a lever C to clamp the brazed joint once the silver solder begins to melt after the current is switched on. When the brazing has been completed the joint needs to be tempered before the saw is put into use; this work is itself carried out in the saw brazer and involves re-heating the brazed joint to a full heat by methods detailed by the manufacturers in their instructions for using the equipment.

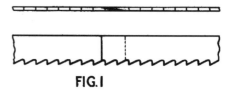

FIG.I

Fig. 1 *Preparing the bandsaw for brazing.*

Once the tempering is complete the joint must be trimmed with a file until it is the same thickness as the rest of the blade itself.

Butt Welding

Of late years, in the interests of time-saving, butt welding has been largely adopted. The equipment involved has provision for the automatic regulation of the whole welding process, that is to say the welding temperature, the pressure applied to the welded joint and the time occupied in the operation is reduced to exact figures that eliminate human error.

Resistance heating, like the method used for brazing the joint, is used to raise the work to welding temperature. Welding is usually initiated manually, after which the complete process of welding and cut-off of current is automatic.

A typical example of the equipment needed is depicted in Fig. 3. This is the Italy 4 now supplied by Wadkin to users

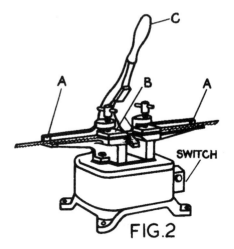

FIG.2

Fig. 2 *A typical bandsaw brazer.*

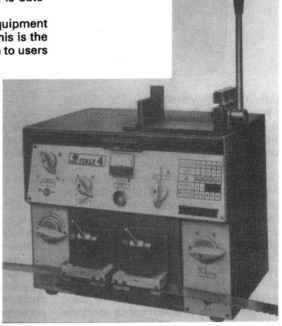

Fig. 3 *Bandsaw butt welding equipment.*

89

mounted cup-shaped grinding wheel affixed to an electric motor may be used. The motor is mounted on a slide and means are provided for adjusting the depth of cut which is made by sliding the rotating guiding wheel over the surface of the welded joint, both sides being ground until the blade presents a smooth finish of uniform thickness.

While bandsaw blades can be sharpened by hand methods and files are available for the purpose, modern practice advises the use of automatic grinding equipment of the type in Fig. 4. The machine seen in the illustration is a product of the Wadkin organisation; it is fully automatic and its controls ensure that the teeth are ground accurately both as to depth and length.

The machine can also be used for sharpening circular saws automatically. Its capacities are:

Circular Saws up to 23⅝" dia.
  (600m/m dia.)
Band Saws up to 2⅜" (60m/m) wide
Maximum Tooth Pitch 1³⁄₁₆" (30m/m)
Maximum Tooth Depth ¾" (19m/m)

Space does not permit a detailed description of the bandsaw grinder being given; suffice it to say that a single motor drives the pivoted grinding head and the cam gear that actuates the feed mechanism as well as the grinding wheel pivoting device.

Handling Bandsaw Blades

It will be appreciated that if unfortunate accidents are not to be forthcoming, some discipline must be practised when bandsaw blades are being handled. Bandsaws have a will of their own, so if they are to be tamed, a rigid procedure must be followed. The methods to be adopted are shown in Fig. 5.

of their bandsaw machines. The various controls are indicated graphically while at the top of the cabinet a guillotine is provided enabling the user to trim the saw ends accurately and speedily.

After welding has taken place the joint needs to be dressed, in order to ensure that the bandsaw blade runs smoothly, particularly over the guide rollers and between the fingers that prevent the blade from twisting when in use.

The dressing may be carried out by filing, using a simple fixture enabling the joint to be held on a slight curve while the filing operation is taking place.

Alternatively the surface of the weld may be ground, in which case a vertically

Fig. 4 (opposite) *The "Loroch" bandsaw grinding machine.*

Fig 4A (right) *Saw sharpening on the Loroch machine.*

Fig. 5 *How to handle a bandsaw blade.*

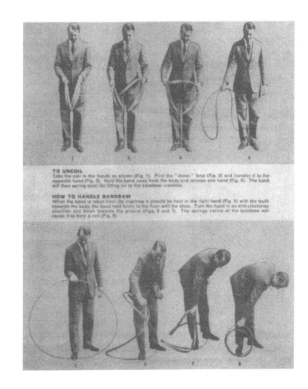

PART 2

Appendix

It has been suggested to the author that drawings of the two miniature hacksaws described in Chapter 1 would be of interest. These two saws, as has been said, are intended to take the 6" blades made by James Neill and marketed under the name 'Eclipse'.

The hacksaw for which the drawings are given in Fig. 1 is probably the simpler of the two devices. The parts

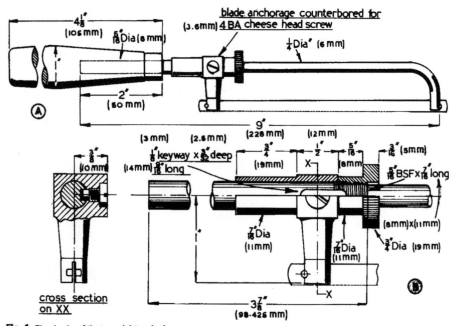

Fig. 1 *The simpler of the two miniature hacksaws.*

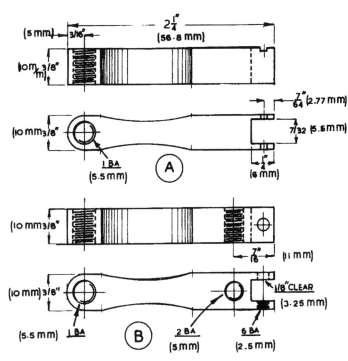

Fig. 2 *The end pieces of the frame for the second saw.*

(5 mm) 3/16"

10 mm 3/8"

2 1/4" (56·8 mm)

7/64" (2.77 mm)

7/32 (5.5 mm)

10 mm 3/8"

1 BA (5.5 mm)

Ⓐ

1/4" (6 mm)

10 mm 3/8"

7/16" (11 mm)

10 mm 3/8"

(5.5 mm) 1 BA

Ⓑ

2 BA (5 mm)

1/8" CLEAR (3·25 mm)

6 BA (2.5 mm)

are not difficult to make, but need good workmanship and careful fitting in order to obtain a satisfactory result.

In Fig. 2, Fig. 3, Fig. 4 and Fig. 4(a) details are given of the second hacksaw. This tool has some parts, in particular those illustrated at A and B, where

a little more mechanical dexterity is required. The main part of the operation is the machining of the waists seen in the drawing. This is work for the fly-cutter, set between centres in the lathe, according to Fig. 5. As will be seen the work is clamped to a vertical slide with

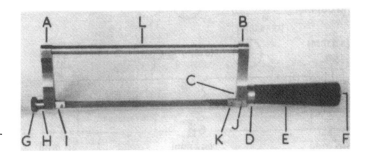

Fig. 2A *The second minia-ture hacksaw.*

93

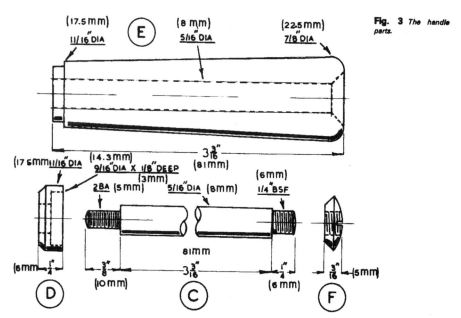

Fig. 3 *The handle parts.*

its own centre to coincide with the axis of the lathe.

The flycutter itself will need to be adjusted to the radius of the curvature required. As in this instance no great accuracy is needed; the point of the flycutting tool can be set with the aid of a rule as depicted in Fig. 6.

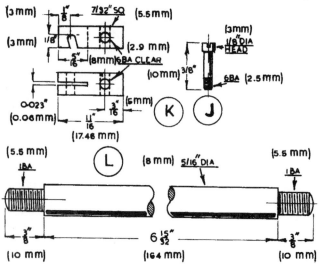

Fig. 4 *The handle-end blade holder and the mainframe spine.*

94

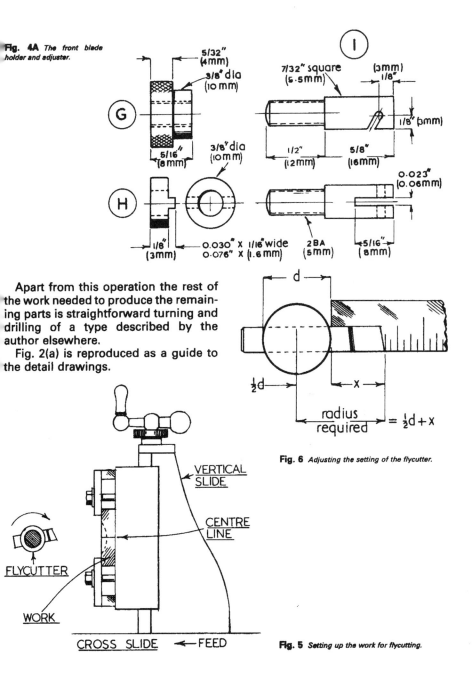

Fig. 4A *The front blade holder and adjuster.*

5/32"
(4mm)

3/8" dia
(10 mm)

G

5/16"
(8mm)

3/8" dia
(10mm)

7/32" square
(5.5mm)

(3mm)
1/8"

1/8" (5mm)

1/2"
(12mm)

5/8"
(16mm)

H

1/8"
(3mm)

0.030" x 1/16" wide
0.076" x (1.6 mm)

0.023"
(0.06mm)

2BA
(5mm)

5/16"
(8mm)

Apart from this operation the rest of the work needed to produce the remaining parts is straightforward turning and drilling of a type described by the author elsewhere.

Fig. 2(a) is reproduced as a guide to the detail drawings.

$$\frac{radius}{required} = \tfrac{1}{2}d + x$$

d

½d

x

Fig. 6 *Adjusting the setting of the flycutter.*

VERTICAL
SLIDE

CENTRE
LINE

FLYCUTTER

WORK

CROSS SLIDE ← FEED

Fig. 5 *Setting up the work for flycutting.*